SINFUL SLIMMING

SINFUL SLIMMING

How to lose weight by eating what you most enjoy

Cas Clarke

Illustrations by
Mike Gordon

Columbus Books
London

To Andy
May your cricket bat never warp

First published in Great Britain in 1987 by
Columbus Books Limited
19-23 Ludgate Hill, London EC4M 7PD

British Library Cataloguing in Publication Data
Clarke, Cas
Sinful slimming: how to lose weight by
eating what you most enjoy.
1. Reducing diets 2. Physical fitness
I. Title
613.2'5 RM222.2

ISBN 0-86287-343-6

Typeset by Cylinder Typesetting Limited
85A Marchmont Street, London

Printed and bound by
The Guernsey Press, Guernsey, Channel Islands

Contents

Introduction

'Do you want to look younger, slimmer, more desirable to your partner?' This must be one of the silliest questions ever asked by the popular press – yet it is asked, in one form or another, at significantly frequent intervals. The fact is that the majority of adults in the affluent Western world are overweight, so it seems a fairly safe bet that the answer to the question must be 'yes'. Almost always the question is asked by way of preface to some new 'miracle' diet – and indeed, it is quite possible that if you were to follow the diet you would indeed see some improvement in your appearance.

But the problem with all diets is that they cannot produce immediate results: they need dedication and a great deal of willpower. Few of us are saints, however, and we find it very hard to refuse that tempting dessert, that piece of cake, that chocolate bar, one or two (alcoholic) drinks. The pleasure we get from these 'treats' is immediate, whilst if we stick to a weight-reducing diet the rewards will be a long time coming – if indeed they ever do come – in the shape of the slimmer, fitter person that we want to be.

The reason why most diets fail is that we are not very good at depriving ourselves of the foods we like over a long period, so we lose heart. But if we knew the diet we were following only had to last a week, at the end of which the fat would have disappeared, never to return, there would be no problem. Many people could manage a week with very little food at all if they knew that afterwards they would never have to worry about their weight again. But a week is not enough. If we really want to gain that new shape, it is as well to realize, right now, at the outset, that it is going to be a *long haul:* there is no such thing as a quick 'miracle' diet.

Assuming that most of us *do* want to be slimmer and fitter, for whatever reason, most of us already know what we should be doing: reducing our food intake and doing a little more exercise. With a lot of willpower, following this regime, the weight should drop off little by little each week. And there lies the stumbling block: it is this item 'willpower' that most of us lack. Inside each saint who starts a diet with good intentions is a sinner just longing to reach for those little calorific goodies – and guess who wins 90 per cent of the time? Saints have willpower; we earthly sinners do not. If *you* had any willpower you wouldn't be reading this book – because you would already be as slim as you wished to be.

So if we lack the magic attribute of willpower (and I know *I* do), what do we do? We accept that we are never going to stick to any diet that denies us all the foods that make life pleasurable. Then, we make a list of the reasons why we are fat. The list might be very long, or quite short: either way, it should enable us to pinpoint our weaknesses. For instance, this is my list:

(1) alcohol
(2) crisps
(3) eating when I'm not hungry
(4) 'snacking' between meals
(5) lack of exercise.

Together these were the reasons why I gained about two stone – not overnight, but probably over a year or two. During my childhood and early teens I was very thin: the proverbial beanpole. When I was fourteen I was desperate to put weight *on*. My weight problem started, I am sure, when I started to socialize. Alcohol is notorious for its fattening qualities, and whilst at university my friends and I consumed it in great quantity. I then became increasingly interested in cooking, and I loved producing new dishes for friends. This is when I started to eat when I was not particularly hungry. My eyes and nose were dictating what I ate – not my appetite.

So over the years I gradually put weight on. At first, although I noticed, I was not particularly worried. I had always been so slim it was not unpleasant to 'round out' a little. And then, as I continued to 'round out', I found that I could not see myself as fat – I had always been slim and therefore always thought of myself as slim (the exact opposite, in fact, of how an anorexic regards herself).

Then at the start of a new year (when I always weigh myself) I found to my horror that I had crept up from 7 stone 10 lb to 9 stone 13 lb (I am 5 feet 4 inches tall) – the fattest I had ever been in my life, and over two stone more than I had been when I left school. This was a real crisis: for the first time I had crept over the edge of the 'acceptable' range in the weight tables. If I didn't do something soon, I would end up as a fat old lady!

This I found totally unacceptable. After all, I was an intelligent young woman with a considerable knowledge of nutrition, so how could I possibly have got into this state? I decided that it was time to treat the problem seriously. I had to identify the reasons why I was getting fat and then discover how I could go about treating them. Over the years I had tried many diets, and had often managed to lose some weight, but it always crept back on. A recent article in a women's magazine reported that 95 per cent of people who have slimmed down to their desirable weight put it back on again, and I was no exception.

So I devised the concept of 'sinful slimming': losing weight without hardship and without the inevitable weight gain after achieving the target weight. The chapters that follow explain how it works, how to keep going despite the fact that you cannot eat at home all the time, how to keep roughly on the straight and narrow when you go out to eat socially, how to entertain without letting your diet go to pot, and, most important, how to maintain your new, wickedly attractive shape once you have achieved it (no point in letting all that effort go to waste). Happy sinning!

1 Sinful Slimming

'Sinful slimming' is a concept that I have evolved to deal with what used to be my own ever-increasing weight problem. Whatever else has been said about dieting, there seems to be one unalterable fact that you cannot get away from: if you eat more than your body requires it will stick around in the form of unwanted fat. Everybody has a different metabolic rate (that is, the rate at which the body converts food into energy) and this sometimes produces the seemingly unfair situation where one person can eat as much as she likes and not put on an ounce whilst another can eat the same amount (or less) yet still put weight on.

However, for every excess 3500 calories we consume over our body's requirement we will add another pound to that fat that we would rather be without – and it is very easy to consume this amount without even trying. So must we count every calorie in an effort to avoid this extra intake? I think that this is unwise. If you really want to *stay* slim – and what is the point of dieting down to your chosen weight and then putting the pounds back on again? – then you do not want to spend the rest of your life counting every calorie that goes into your mouth. Instead, try to cultivate a more wary attitude to food. It is worth while finding out just how many calories some foodstuffs contain – then at least you will have a better idea of what you should cut down on – notice that I say 'cut down', not 'cut out' altogether. To stay slim when you have lost your required amount of weight you must start to cultivate certain changes in your present diet, because it is your present diet that has got you into trouble. I want to help you learn how to sin enough to enjoy yourself but not enough to get into trouble.

Of course, you have to *pay* for your sins – and the price of sinful slimming is that it is a slow process. However, the compensating factors are that there is no reason why you should not enjoy your diet, and that once lost the weight is likely to stay off. Strangely enough, it is very easy to do once you get the hang of it.

The idea is to cut your main meals down to a reasonable level and establish a healthy diet, then give yourself an allowance that you can use for the foods you really like. This makes dieting much easier. It is nice knowing that you don't have to give up everything that you most enjoy.

To lose weight, women should keep their calorie intake down to 1000-1200 calories a day (men need slightly more, say 1500). This will allow for a varied and healthy diet, as long as the meals are sensibly chosen, and depending on how overweight you already are, it will still allow you a reasonable amount to cheat with.

This, then, is what sinful slimming is all about – following a sensible eating plan that will show you how to choose foods that are both good to eat and good for your health and figure, yet still allow you a certain amount of leeway to eat what you like – however unhealthy! I have called this allowance Cheat Units. When you have lost your desired amount of weight your eating habits will have changed as you have learnt what foods are good for you and which you should restrict. You may well find that you enjoy these restricted foods more when you are only allowed them occasionally; others find that they lose all desire for them: everybody is different and reacts in different ways.

Personally, I find that it is wise to give in to any really powerful desire I may have for a particular food, otherwise I suffer hours of anguish – usually culminating in a massive binge which I could have avoided had I not tried to be a martyr.

Sinful slimming may sound like a strangely painless way to lose weight, but it has worked for me and many of my friends, so I hope you will try it and see it work for you. When I gained my unwanted extra two stone, it took me four to five months to regain my former weight of 7 stone 10 lb. Not fast, but I did get there.

I now follow a maintenance diet which I have worked out to accommodate my lifestyle. It consists of a sensible eating plan which, if I never eat anything else, would result in my continuing to lose weight. But of course now that I have lost the weight that I set out to lose I can have a few extras without straying far off the weight that I want to be. I'm no longer losing or gaining weight, yet I don't have to count calories or refrain from eating the foods I enjoy. If I want to go out for a meal, I can. If I want to indulge in a piece of chocolate cake, I can. If this sounds like your sort of diet – read on!

2 Establishing Sinful Ways

So now that you know what sinful slimming is all about, how do you get started? First, establish from the weight/height charts what your ideal weight should be: this is your weight without clothes. Add 2-3 lb for clothes. Notice that I have only given the range of suitable weights for your height – only *you* can judge what weight will suit you best, as you know how you want to look when you finish. After all, there is no point becoming a beanpole if your boyfriend prefers curves . . . And if you are male, why keeping dieting when you know that your girlfriend prefers you hunky rather than weedy? Be sensible and use your own judgement to choose a weight that you know you will look good at. (Remember, it is not a crime to change your mind at a later date.)

Then decide how much cheating you think you need to incorporate into your diet to allow you to keep to it.

The best way to do this is to look at what you eat now and then count up the things that you really like and know are fattening, e.g. chocolate bars, cream cakes, an excess of butter on vegetables, crisps, alcoholic drinks, biscuits and cakes, rich or fatty foods. Compare these to the items on the Cheat Charts and work out how many Cheat Units you currently consume each week.

If your favourite 'baddies' are not on my list find out from the calorie guide at the end of the book how many calories your baddies contain and divide by 100 to find out the number of Cheat Units you normally use up.

Then, depending on how overweight you are, decide how many Cheat Units you are going to allow yourself each week. Probably the more overweight you are the more cheating you already do. If you *do* already cheat a lot you would be silly to try to break that habit too quickly. It is hardly realistic to think that if you already consume three chocolate bars a day you can cut this down overnight to three bars a week!

If you have many weaknesses – a cheese roll as a mid-morning snack, a chocolate bar in the afternoon and then a few drinks to unwind with in the evening, you must decide what you enjoy most and decide to spend your Cheat Units on that. Moderation is the answer, not martyrdom. So the more overweight you are, the more Cheat Units you will want to start off with: otherwise you will soon start feeling deprived. But don't forget that the more Cheat Units you incorporate into your diet, the slower will be your weight loss.

Once you have decided what your ideal weight would be and how much you want to cheat, refer to the Time Chart to find out how long you should expect it to take for you to gain your new shape. This will probably give you a shock. That new shape may be a long way away – so far away that you may be tempted to reduce your Cheat Units to shorten this period of time. However, think twice about this, for *you* are the one who will have to live with this diet and if you make it too strict you will soon find that the effort of sticking to it demands superhuman dedication of the kind you have already admitted you don't have. Better to have an easy diet you can keep to than a difficult one that is likely to over-stretch your willpower.

Height/weight tables

Women

Height (imperial)	**(metric)**	**Weight range (imperial)**	**(metric)**
4 ft 10 inches	1.47 metres	6 st 8 lb – 8 st 7 lb	41.7 kg – 54.0 kg
4 ft 11 inches	1.50 metres	6 st 10 lb – 8 st 10 lb	42.5 kg – 55.2 kg
5 ft	1.52 metres	6 st 12 lb – 8 st 13 lb	43.4 kg – 56.7 kg
5 ft 1 inch	1.55 metres	7 st 1 lb – 9 st 2 lb	44.8 kg – 58.0 kg
5 ft 2 inches	1.58 metres	7 st 4 lb – 9 st 5 lb	46.2 kg – 59.3 kg
5 ft 3 inches	1.60 metres	7 st 7 lb – 7 st 8 lb	47.6 kg – 60.8 kg
5 ft 4 inches	1.63 metres	7 st 10 lb – 9 st 12 lb	48.9 kg – 62.6 kg
5 ft 5 inches	1.65 metres	7 st 13 lb – 10 st 2 lb	50.3 kg – 64.4 kg
5 ft 6 inches	1.68 metres	8 st 2 lb – 10 st 6 lb	51.6 kg – 66.2 kg
5 ft 7 inches	1.70 metres	8 st 6 lb – 10 st 10 lb	53.5 kg – 68.0 kg
5 ft 8 inches	1.73 metres	8 st 10 lb – 11 st	55.3 kg – 69.8 kg
5 ft 9 inches	1.75 metres	9 st 0 lb – 11 st 4 lb	57.1 kg – 71.6 kg
5 ft 10 inches	1.78 metres	9 st 4 lb – 11 st 9 lb	59.4 kg – 73.4 kg
5 ft 11 inches	1.80 metres	9 st 8 lb – 12 st	61.2 kg – 76.2 kg
6 ft	1.83 metres	9 st 12 lb – 12 st 5 lb	63.4 kg – 78.9 kg

Men

Height (imperial)	**(metric)**	**Weight range (imperial)**	**(metric)**
5 ft 2 inches	1.57 metres	8 st – 10 st 1 lb	50.8 kg – 63.9 kg
5 ft 3 inches	1.60 metres	8 st 3 lb – 10 st 4 lb	52.1 kg – 65.3 kg
5 ft 4 inches	1.63 metres	8 st 6 lb – 10 st 8 lb	53.5 kg – 67.1 kg
5 ft 5 inches	1.65 metres	8 st 9 lb – 10 st 12 lb	54.8 kg – 68.9 kg
5 ft 6 inches	1.68 metres	8 st 12 lb – 11 st 2 lb	56.2 kg – 70.7 kg
5 ft 7 inches	1.70 metres	9 st 2 lb – 11 st 7 lb	58.0 kg – 73.0 kg
5 ft 8 inches	1.73 metres	9 st 6 lb – 11 st 12 lb	59.8 kg – 75.2 kg
5 ft 9 inches	1.75 metres	9 st 10 lb – 12 st 2 lb	61.6 kg – 77.0 kg
5 ft 10 inches	1.78 metres	10 st – 12 st 6 lb	63.5 kg – 78.8 kg
5 ft 11 inches	1.80 metres	10 st 4 lb – 12 st 11 lb	65.3 kg – 81.2 kg
6 ft	1.83 metres	10 st 8 lb – 13 st 2 lb	67.1 kg – 83.4 kg
6 ft 1 inch	1.85 metres	10 st 12 lb – 13 st 7 lb	68.9 kg – 85.7 kg
6 ft 2 inches	1.88 metres	11 st 2 lb – 13 st 12 lb	70.7 kg – 87.9 kg
6 ft 3 inches	1.91 metres	11 st 6 lb – 14 st 3 lb	72.5 kg – 90.1 kg
6 ft 4 inches	1.93 metres	11 st 10 lb – 14 st 8 lb	74.3 kg – 92.4 kg

To get an idea of how much your cheat allowance is worth consult this list of Cheat Units: it will show you what you could allow yourself each day/week. The left-hand column shows how much weight (very roughly) you would lose if you were to deny yourself this indulgence.

Cheat Chart

Weight	**Cheat Units**	**Vice**
½ oz/15 g	1	1 glass white wine (5 fl oz/150 ml)
1½ oz/45 g	3	½ bottle wine (3 glasses)
3½ oz/105 g	7	1 glass white wine daily for a week (7 glasses)
6½ oz/195 g	13	2 glasses white wine daily for a week (14 glasses)
5 oz/150g	10	2 evenings' drinking (10 drinks)
1 oz/30 g	2	1½ oz/45 g blue stilton
2 oz/60 g	4	1 cheese and pickle sandwich (made with 2 slices of bread)
2½ oz/75 g	5	1 ¼-lb hamburger
3 oz/90 g	6	2 chocolate bars, e.g. Bounty, Twix, Marathon
7 oz/210 g	14	5 chocolate bars, e.g. Bounty, Twix, Marathon
4 oz/120 g	8	2 milkshakes (10 fl oz/250 ml)
4½ oz/135 g	9	1 large cheeseburger and large portion chips
5½ oz/165 g	11	5 cream doughnuts
6 oz/180 g	12	½ packet chocolate digestive biscuits (say, 12 large biscuits)
7½ oz/225 g	15	5 crispy cheese rolls
8 oz/240 g	16	Indian meal, e.g. 1 portion curry, 1 portion rice, 1 poppadum, 1 tablespoon/15 ml chutney

This is only a rough guide: discover the calorie count of any baddies to which you are particularly addicted and divide that figure by 100 to find out how many Cheat Units to allow each time you indulge in your own vice.

Cheat Unit allowances

Look at the weight range that you are presently in and find your recommended number of Cheat Units per week. This is the number that would suit you best. You can decide on any number from within the range shown, but you *must* keep within this range.

Weight	**Cheat Unit recommendation**	**Cheat Unit range**
8 st+	7	7–14
8 st 7 lb	14	7–21
9 st+	14	7–21
9 st 7 lb	21	14–28
10 st+	21	14–28
10 st 7 lb	21	14–28
11 st+	21	14–28
11 st 7 lb	28	21–35
12 st+	28	21–35
12 st 7 lb	28	21–35
13 st+	28	21–35
13 st 7 lb	28	21–35
14 st+	28	21–35

Try to stick to the recommended Cheat Units for your present weight, unless you have been trying to diet for a long time: if that is the case, allow yourself more units. If in any doubt about how many to start with, go for a higher amount and reduce it if you find that you can get by with less. *Do stay in the range given for your weight:* this has been calculated to maintain a steady weight loss without letting you feel hungry – which would lead to your overeating.

If you were on a normal diet that allowed you about 1000 calories daily you would expect to lose about 2 lb weekly, *if* you were strong-willed enough to keep to it. 'Sinful slimming' is based on that same daily calorie allowance with the addition of the Cheat Units which make the diet a lot easier to stick to. This of course means that you will lose weight more slowly – but isn't it better to take a few months to lose that weight than never to lose it at all? Also, weight which is lost slowly is thought to be easier to keep off than that lost on a quick-loss diet.

When I was 9 stone 13, I wanted to slim down to 8 stone 7

– I needed to shed 20 lb. On a normal diet I would have aimed to lose that over 10–11 weeks, but I knew that I would not want to give up my social drinking and that I would want the odd packet of crisps too; I also wanted to be able to eat out with friends on occasion. So I gave myself an allowance of 28 cheat units a week, or 4 a day. That meant I would *not* be losing 2 ounces a day, as I might on the regular slimming diet (140 ounces over 10 weeks), but that extra allowance had made it possible for me to stick to the diet. It took me 17 weeks to get down to my ideal weight – but it was certainly worth while, and I did not feel deprived whilst I was losing that weight. I had carried on my normal social life and continued with a normal varied diet. Having started early in the year, I was in fine health and shape for summer.

So if you wish to reach your ideal weight, follow my example: determine your ideal weight and subtract this from your present weight (remember there are 14 lb in a stone); decide on the number of Cheat Units you wish to allow yourself each week, then look down the Time Chart to find the number of pounds you wish to lose; look along that row to the heading that corresponds with the number of Cheat Units you have decided on; this will tell you how many weeks you will need to lose this weight.

Time chart for weight loss

See opposite page. 'X' in the Cheat Unit column means that it is not advisable to allow yourself this number of Cheat Units to lose this amount of weight.

Shocked to find out how long your weight loss could take? Don't forget that it is better to take a long time and lose that weight permanently rather than start another diet that is doomed to failure. Happy dieting!

lbs to lose	No. of Cheat Units (per week) 7	14	21	28	35
	No. of weeks it will take to lose this weight				
7	4	5	5	6	7
8	5	5	6	7	8
9	5	6	7	8	9
10	6	7	8	9	10
11	6	7	8	9	11
12	7	8	9	10	12
13	7	8	9	11	13
14	8	9	10	12	14
15	9	10	11	13	15
16	9	10	12	14	16
17	10	11	13	15	17
18	10	12	13	15	18
19	11	12	14	16	19
20	11	13	15	17	20
21	12	14	15	18	21
22	13	14	16	19	22
23	13	15	17	20	23
24	14	15	17	20	24
25	14	16	18	21	25
26	15	17	19	22	26
27	15	17	20	23	27
28	16	18	20	24	28
29	17	19	21	25	29
30	17	19	22	25	30
31	18	20	22	26	31
32	18	20	23	27	32
33	19	21	24	28	33
34	19	22	25	29	34
35	20	22	25	30	35
36	X	X	26	30	36
37	X	X	27	31	37
38	X	X	28	32	38
39	X	X	28	33	39
40	X	X	29	34	40
41	X	X	30	34	41
42	X	X	30	35	42
43	X	X	31	36	43
44	X	X	32	37	44
45	X	X	33	38	45
46	X	X	33	39	46
47	X	X	34	39	47
48	X	X	35	40	48
49	X	X	35	41	49
50	X	X	36	42	50
51	X	X	37	43	51

3 Staying a Sinner

Have you ever noticed that as soon as you mention that you are on a diet everyone goes out of their way to offer you fattening foods – or tell you not to be silly, you look fine as you are? Infuriating, isn't it?

There is a very simple answer to this problem: just don't tell anyone that you are on a diet. If you are following the 'sinful slimming' diet this is easy to comply with because you will sometimes be eating foods that are generally considered fattening, so no one will suspect that you are on a diet. It will also save you all sorts of explanations when people catch you eating cream cakes (or whatever your own particular vice is!) and triumphantly cry, 'But I thought you said you were on a diet!' You can really do without this sort of hassle, so don't let on to anyone that you are trying to lose weight. If anyone *does* notice that you aren't eating your usual quota of ten chocolate bars a day or quaffing pints of beer every night, just say that you are trying to eat more healthily – but don't mention the word 'diet' if you want a quiet life.

The diets in this book are very easy to follow, as they are well balanced and the meals are filling. The problem with 'staying a sinner' is simply how you control your Cheat Units. If you continually over-indulge with these you will not lose weight without divine intervention – and it's a little risky to count on that. The Cheat Units are there to make sure that you do not feel that you are on a diet, which is very important psychologically. Have you noticed that as soon as you go on a diet you become very conscious of food and are forever thinking about your next meal? Try not to think of yourself as dieting and therefore depriving yourself of food: just regard the diet as a new way of eating that you enjoy. Life would soon become pretty miserable if you were to start saying 'no' to every social excursion that involves eating or drinking. If it is someone's birthday and a tasty cake is going round, why shouldn't you too have a piece?

It is also unnecessary to count every calorie. You will, after all, know roughly how many times you have strayed from the straight and narrow. If you know you are going to spend the evening in the pub, you might wish to give up the little treat you fancy earlier in the day to make up for it. The trick is not to give up *all* your vices but to decide which ones are most important to your enjoying yourself. You may not be able to have everything in life but it is true that a little of what you fancy does you good!

Another way to make life easier is to make sure that you are taking full advantage of all the low-calorie alternatives that are available. Many food and drink items nowadays have a low-calorie, low-fat, no-added-sugar or similar equivalent. Why use ordinary mayonnaise or salad cream on your baked potato or salad when the fat-reduced alternative is every bit as tasty and contains far fewer calories? If you must have fat on your vegetables use a low-fat spread, not butter. Try the new cream substitutes on the market as an alternative to cooking with real cream, or use low-fat yoghurt. There are now many varieties of low-fat or reduced-fat cheeses on the market and these are the types I have specified in my recipes. If however you cannot find these in your local shops you could substitute Edam, which is almost as low in calories as these special cheeses. Always choose low-calorie diet drinks rather than ordinary coke or lemonade: in hot weather you would be amazed how many calories this can save you.

Some people say that they can taste the difference between low-calorie alternatives and the 'real thing', and it is true that some do have a slightly different taste. There is a noticeable difference between full-cream milk and skimmed milk, for example. However, be assured that if you persevere you will get used to the alternative, and then, when you come to taste the 'real thing', you will find it too rich for your re-educated tastebuds.

It is when you have reached this stage that you will realize that your battle is nearly won, and that you are unlikely to return to your old ways of eating.

And do not forget that your diet is not only important to how you look. It is of prime importance to your health. We all now accept that the ideal diet should be high in fibre, low in fat, salt and sugar, and capable of supplying the body with the protein, minerals and vitamins that it needs to perform efficiently.

Doctors are increasingly warning women, in particular, to maintain the level of calcium in their diets. Calcium is essential for strong bones and lack of calcium in the twenties and thirties can lead to brittle bones in later life. Skimmed milk contains as much calcium as full-fat milk and is one item in your diet on which you should never cut down.

One word here about another important aspect of keeping fit and healthy: exercise. If you are overweight you are probably very resistant to the thought of exercise. However, for your own good you should try to include some sort of regular exercise in your lifestyle. The easiest thing to start off with is walking. Try to get out and about two or three times a week. You don't have to go on a marathon – just go out and set up the routine of doing something that tones up the muscles. Later you might go swimming once a week – a chance to show off your new figure!

My favourite exercise is one I thoroughly recommend: using a mini-trampoline or rebounder. Ten minutes' bouncing on this does wonders for your health and shape – and all in the privacy of your home. (Do ensure, however, before trying this, that your floorboards are sound.) Even though I am no fan of exercise even *I* have found this an easy discipline to keep up. In the end you will only stick at something that you enjoy doing, so don't choose a form of exercise you know you hate. On the other hand, don't cop out altogether and do nothing: if you try hard enough you must find *something* physical that you enjoy doing. (And if you really can't think of anything at all, try changing your partner!)

It has been a great pleasure to me to realize as I write this that at long last I don't have to worry about my weight any more. It is firmly under control, even if I have succumbed to the occasional eating binge – for instance, when friends have stayed the weekend – and put on a few pounds. I know that my weight quickly returns to normal just by keeping an eye on the extras that I have. After a prolonged eating bout, however (for example, Christmas or a summer holiday), I recommend sticking to the basic diet with a maximum allowance of only 7 Cheat Units a week to allow yourself to get quickly back to normal.

By the time you get to your Judgement Day (the day by which you should have reached your target weight), you will find that it is easy to follow the maintenance diets without even thinking about them – and then your weight problem really will be a thing of the past.

4 Everyday Eating

To be sure that you eat a healthy, balanced diet you should always vary your menus. Even if you have a favourite meal, it should not appear too often in your diet. Variety should ensure that you receive all the many vitamins and minerals that your body needs to keep it healthy. It is now recognized that a healthy diet is one which is low in fat, salt and sugar and high in fibre. For this reason many people are now including vegetarian meals in their diet, for these tend to fulfil all these criteria. Vegetarian or not, many people are now eating less red meat, which has a high saturated fat content, or are switching to leaner cuts. Fish and chicken consumption are on the increase as these are both low in fat (as long as the skin is removed from the chicken). Consumption of hard cheeses and full-fat dairy produce should also be reduced to ensure a healthy diet. Many dairy products are now available in a reduced-fat or low-fat version – a boon to people who wish to change to a healthier way of eating, and to slimmers. If you follow these guidelines *and* limit your alcohol intake – and stop smoking – you will make yourself a much healthier person.

Your basic daily allowance is:
(1) breakfast, lunch, dinner and 2 side dishes;
(2) 10 fl oz (300 ml) skimmed milk, for use in tea or coffee or as a late-night drink. This allowance is in addition to any milk listed in the recipes that follow.

Divide your Cheat Units up over the whole week, either allowing yourself a daily treat or saving them all for a binge at the weekend.

Men should double the quantities of protein and filler foods in the dinner recipes, i.e. the amount of meat, fish or pulses and the amounts of pasta, rice, potatoes and bread they eat. They can also add a piece of fresh fruit, e.g. an apple or orange, to their daily intake.

Eating at home

Breakfasts

One of the best breakfasts that you can have is cereal with skimmed milk and perhaps a little fruit added. However, I have suggested some other breakfast menus as alternatives. If you really are happy to miss breakfast, go ahead but have a snack later instead. Don't substitute a chocolate bar for breakfast – this meal is important for getting fibre into your diet.

Cereal

1-1½ oz (25-40 g) breakfast cereal
5 fl oz (150 ml) skimmed milk

Yoghurt and toast

1 small carton low-fat yoghurt
1 apple

1 small slice wholemeal bread
2 teaspoons (10 ml) jam

Core the apple and cut into small chunks. Add to the yoghurt. Follow with the toasted bread spread with jam.

Grapefruit and toast

½ medium grapefruit

2 small slices wholemeal bread
4 teaspoons (20 ml) jam

Serve the grapefruit and follow with the toasted bread spread with jam.

Fruity porridge

1 oz (25 g) porridge oats
4 tablespoons (60 ml) skimmed milk
1 teaspoon (5 ml) brown sugar
1 tablespoon (15 ml) raisins

Make the porridge with water and serve with the raisins and skimmed milk mixed in and sprinkled with the sugar.

Grapefruit and egg

½ medium grapefruit

1 small soft-boiled egg
1 small slice wholemeal bread
1 teaspoon (5 ml) yeast extract

Serve the grapefruit. Follow with the egg and the toasted bread spread with the yeast extract.

Baked bean breakfast

2 small slices wholemeal bread
4 oz (100 g) baked beans

Serve the heated beans with the toasted bread.

Weekend specials

Bacon, beans and mushrooms

3½ oz (100 g) bacon steak, well grilled
1 small slice wholemeal bread
3½ oz (100 g) sugar-free baked beans
3 medium button mushrooms, grilled or poached

Serve the bacon steak with the toasted bread, topped with the baked beans and accompanied by the mushrooms.

Sausage, egg and beans

1 small egg
1 tablespoon (15 ml) skimmed milk
1 low-fat sausage, well grilled
3½ oz (100 g) sugar-free baked beans

Scramble the egg in a non-stick frying-pan with the milk. Serve with the sausage and beans.

Bacon, mushrooms and tomato

4 oz (100 g) mushrooms
1 tablespoon (15 ml) tomato purée
dash Worcestershire sauce
2 rashers streaky bacon, well grilled
1 small slice wholemeal bread
1 large tomato

Roughly cut the mushrooms and heat with the tomato purée and Worcestershire sauce. Serve the bacon, topped with the mushroom mixture, on the toasted bread. Halve and grill the tomato for garnish.

Lunches

SOUPS

Vegetable soup

10-oz (250-g) can thick vegetable, lentil or pea and ham soup
2 small slices wholemeal bread

Heat the soup and serve with the bread.

Baked bean soup

7½-oz (200-g) can sugar-free baked beans
2 teaspoons (10 ml) tomato purée
dash Worcestershire sauce
5 fl oz (150 ml) water
2 small slices wholemeal bread

Purée the first 4 ingredients, heat gently, then serve with the bread.

Home-made vegetable soup

8-oz (200-g) can tomatoes
4 oz (100 g) cooked diced potatoes
4 oz (100 g) cooked diced carrots
2 tablespoons (30 ml) cooked peas
salt and pepper
2 small slices wholemeal bread

Purée the tomatoes and half the potatoes together. Add the rest of the potatoes, the carrots and peas. Season, then heat gently and serve with the bread.

SANDWICHES

These sandwiches can all be followed with a piece of fresh fruit, such as an apple, or a handful (2 oz/50 g) of grapes, to make a good, balanced and sustaining meal.

Pâté sandwich

3 small slices wholemeal bread
1½ oz (35 g) low-fat liver pâté or
1½ oz (35 g) meat paste
lettuce, cucumber, grated carrot, grated courgette,
sliced tomato
pepper

Spread the bread with the low-fat liver pâté or meat paste. Top two slices with your chosen salad ingredients. Season with pepper and sandwich the slices together.

Tomato and sardine sandwich

3 small slices wholemeal bread
1½ oz (35 g) tomato and sardine paste
lettuce, sliced cucumber
pepper

Spread the bread with the paste and fill with lettuce and cucumber. Season with pepper.

Cheese sandwich

3 small slices wholemeal bread
1 oz (25 g) cheese spread (2 triangles)
1 celery stick, finely chopped
lettuce

Spread the bread with the cheese spread mixed with the chopped celery, add the lettuce and sandwich the slices together.

Tuna roll

2 oz (50 g) tuna canned in brine, drained
1 teaspoon (5 ml) low-calorie mayonnaise
1 wholemeal roll
chopped Chinese leaves
sliced cucumber
pepper

Mix together the tuna and the mayonnaise. Fill the roll with this mixture, the Chinese leaves and the cucumber. Season with pepper.

Ham roll

2 teaspoons (10 ml) low-fat spread
1 wholemeal roll
1 slice lean ham, trimmed
mustard

Spread the low-fat spread on the roll. Add the ham and mustard.

Cheese roll

1 wholemeal roll
2 teaspoons (10 ml) low-fat spread
1 oz (25 g) low-fat cheese, grated
lettuce
sliced cucumber

Spread the roll with the low-fat spread and then fill with the cheese, lettuce and cucumber.

Tuna and pasta salad

1 oz (25 g) wholemeal pasta, cooked
2 oz (50 g) tuna canned in brine, drained
1 tablespoon (15 ml) cooked peas
1 tablespoon (15 ml) low-calorie seafood dressing
lettuce, sliced cucumber, diced pepper, grated courgette, chopped celery

Toss the first 4 ingredients together and serve on a bed of the selected salad ingredients.

Cheese and sweetcorn salad

1 oz (25 g) wholemeal pasta, cooked
1 oz (25 g) low-fat cheese, diced
1 tablespoon (15 ml) sweetcorn
1 tablespoon (15 ml) low-fat garlic or blue-cheese dressing
grated carrot, grated red cabbage, diced red pepper, grated white cabbage, chopped celery

Toss together the first 4 ingredients and serve on a bed of the selected salad ingredients.

Potato and cheese salad

4 oz (100 g) cooked potato, diced
1 oz (25 g) low-fat cheese, diced
1 tablespoon (15 ml) low-calorie mayonnaise
1 tablespoon (15 ml) skimmed milk
grated courgette, Chinese leaves, sliced green pepper, sliced fennel, watercress

Toss together the first 4 ingredients and serve on a bed of the selected salad ingredients.

Cottage cheese and sweetcorn salad

4-oz (100-g) carton cottage cheese
1 oz (25 g) low-fat blue cheese, diced
1 tablespoon (15 ml) sweetcorn
Chinese leaves, chopped celery, grated courgette, diced green pepper, chopped cucumber

Toss together the first 3 ingredients and serve on a bed of the selected salad ingredients.

Mixed salad lunch

3½ oz (100 g) canned red kidney beans
1 tablespoon (15 ml) sweetcorn
1 tablespoon (15 ml) cooked peas
1 tablespoon (15 ml) low-calorie french dressing
sprinkling mixed herbs
Chinese leaves, sliced cucumber, chopped fennel, diced green pepper, grated carrot, grated white cabbage

Toss the first 5 ingredients together and serve on a bed of the selected salad ingredients.

Butter bean salad

3½ oz (100 g) canned butter beans
1 tablespoon (15 ml) sweetcorn)
1 tablespoon (15 ml) cooked peas
1 tablespoon (15 ml) low-calorie mayonnaise
1 tablespoon (15 ml) skimmed milk
Chinese leaves, lettuce, chopped cucumber, watercress, diced green pepper

Toss together the first 5 ingredients and serve on a bed of the selected salad ingredients.

COOKED SNACKS

Baked beans on toast

2 small slices wholemeal bread
7½ oz (200 g) sugar-free baked beans

Toast the bread and serve the beans on top.

Fish fingers

2 fish fingers, grilled or baked
4 oz (100 g) potato, cooked and mashed with
 2 tablespoons (30 ml) skimmed milk
2 tablespoons (30 ml) cooked peas
1 tablespoon (15 ml) tomato ketchup

Serve the fish fingers with the mash and peas accompanied by the tomato ketchup.

Fish cake

1 fish cake, grilled or baked
7½ oz (200 g) sugar-free baked beans
4 oz (100 g) mushrooms, grilled or baked

Serve the fish cake with the baked beans and mushrooms.

Beefburgers

2 low-fat beefburgers, well grilled
3½ oz (100 g) sugar-free baked beans
1 tablespoon (15 ml) cooked peas

Serve the beefburgers with the beans and peas.

Spaghetti on toast

7½-oz (200-g) can spaghetti or wholemeal pasta
 in tomato sauce
2 small slices wholemeal bread.

Heat the spaghetti and serve on the toasted bread.

Saucy cod

1 packet cod-in-sauce
4 oz (100 g) cooked new potatoes
2 tablespoons (30 ml) cooked peas

Cook the cod-in-sauce as directed on the packet and serve with the potatoes and peas.

Dinners

Menus in this section are arranged according to their main ingredient: chicken, fish, pulses, pasta, rice, potato, bread and so on. A section on side dishes follows, divided into hot and cold.

Having chosen your main dish, add two side dishes. Do not add anything else, unless of course your own private vice is tomato sauce or sweet pickle – which of course you will have allowed for in your Cheat Unit quota. I have to admit that this is something *I* cannot do without – I love something spicy on the side, especially with curries. Though I prefer my curries fairly mild, I like to add a little lime pickle to pep them up, so I can alternate the tastes of the mild curry with the hot and spicy lime pickle.

CHICKEN

Chinese chicken

3 oz (75 g) boned chicken breast, without skin
1 oz (25 g) hoisin sauce
4 oz (100 g) canned bamboo shoots, sliced
2 oz (50 g) egg noodles
chopped spring onions to garnish

Slice the chicken breast very finely, then stir-fry the chicken, sauce and bamboo shoots for 1 minute or until the chicken is cooked. Serve on the boiled egg noodles. Garnish with the onion.

Italian chicken

6 oz (150 g) boned chicken breast
7 oz (175 g) canned tomatoes
1 tablespoon (15 ml) tomato purée
oregano
1 oz (25 g) pasta shells

Remove the skin from the chicken, then make 3-4 gashes in the flesh. Drain the tomatoes and chop. Mix the tomatoes with the purée and the oregano and spread over the top of the chicken. Cover with foil and bake at 200°C/400°F/Gas 6 for 45 minutes. Serve with the cooked pasta.

Chicken cranberry

8 oz (200 g) chicken leg joint
4 oz (100 g) boiled potatoes
1 tablespoon (15 ml) cranberry sauce

Remove the skin from the chicken and grill well. Serve with hot boiled potatoes and cranberry sauce.

French chicken

6 oz (150 g) boned chicken breast
1 teaspoon (5 ml) french mustard
1 oz (25 g) brown long-grain rice
1 tablespoon (15 ml) cooked peas
1 tablespoon (15 ml) cooked sweetcorn

Remove the skin from the chicken. Grill one side until cooked, then grill the other side spread with mustard. Boil the rice and mix with the peas and sweetcorn. Serve with the grilled chicken.

Chicken jambalaya

8 oz (200 g) chicken leg joint
3 oz (75 g) banana
1 oz (25 g) brown long-grain rice
1 tablespoon (15 ml) sweetcorn

Remove the skin from the chicken and grill well. When cooked, slice the banana, place on top of the chicken and grill lightly until just softening. Boil the rice and mix with the sweetcorn. Serve with the chicken.

FISH

Trout with potatoes moutarde

6 oz (150 g) whole trout (cleaned, head removed if preferred)
4 oz (100 g) potatoes
1 teaspoon (5 ml) low-fat spread
1 teaspoon (5 ml) french mustard

Grill the trout on both sides until cooked. Boil the potatoes and mix with low-fat spread and mustard. Serve with the trout.

Stuffed fish

6 oz (150 g) white fish fillet
2 oz (50 g) chopped mushrooms
1 tablespoon (15 ml) prepared stuffing (from a packet)
2 oz (50 g) potatoes, boiled
1 oz (25 g) sour cream
1 tablespoon (15 ml) skimmed milk
ground black pepper

Flatten the fish, then mix the mushrooms and the stuffing together and place in the middle of the fish. Roll the fish round the stuffing. Put in a greased ovenproof dish. Slice the cooked potatoes and cover the fish with them. Mix the cream and milk together and pour over the potato. Season with pepper. Bake in a pre-heated oven at 200°C/400°F/Gas 6 for 30 minutes.

Smoked mackerel

5 oz (125 g) small smoked mackerel
3 oz (75 g) boiled potatoes
1 tablespoon (15 ml) creamed horseradish sauce

Grill the mackerel for a few minutes to heat through, then serve with the potatoes and the creamed horseradish sauce.

Fish kebab

4 oz (100 g) monkfish
2 oz (50 g) peeled scampi
2 oz (50 g) scallop
1 diced red pepper
1 teaspoon (5 ml) low-fat spread
sprinkling chopped parsley
1 oz (25 g) long-grain rice

Cube the monkfish and cut the scampi and scallop into bite-sized pieces. Thread the fish and the pepper alternately on to 2 small skewers (or 1 large one if you have a large grill). Melt the low-fat spread and add the parsley. Brush this over the fish, then grill for a few minutes until the fish is cooked. Serve on the boiled rice.

Curried prawns

2 oz (50 g) shelled prawns
4 oz (100 g) thick yoghurt
1 tablespoon (15 ml) tomato purée
1 teaspoon (5 ml) mild curry paste
1 oz (25 g) long-grain rice

Mix the first 4 ingredients together, then heat through gently. Serve with the boiled rice.

PULSES

Pulses make exceedingly good slimming fare, being nutritious, high in fibre and low in fat. Don't write them off as something eaten only by fully paid-up vegetarians. So, be adventurous: even if you have never eaten dishes of this sort before, try one or two – I'm sure you will be pleasantly surprised.

Shepherdess pie

2 oz (50 g) red lentils
1 small chopped onion
1 teaspoon (5 ml) oil
1 tablespoon (15 ml) tomato purée
3 oz (75 g) boiled potato
1 teaspoon (5 ml) skimmed milk
1 diced red pepper
dash soy sauce

Quickly fry the lentils and the onion in the oil, then add the tomato purée and cover with just enough water to top the mixture. Boil, then simmer for 10 minutes. Mash the potato with the milk. Then grease a small ovenproof dish and put the lentils, red pepper and soy sauce into this. Cover with the mash and bake at 180°C/350°F/Gas 4 for 20 minutes.

Bean and cheese crumble

2 oz (50 g) mixed red kidney beans and blackeye beans, soaked overnight
2 oz (50 g) carrots
2 oz (50 g) swede
1 tablespoon (15 ml) tomato purée
7 oz (175 g) canned tomatoes
sprinkling oregano
soy sauce
1 small slice wholemeal bread, crumbled
1 oz (25 g) reduced-fat cheese, thinly grated

Cook the beans in boiling water for 45 minutes or until soft. Drain and dice. Cook the carrot and swede. Mix with the beans, purée, tomatoes and seasonings. Place in an ovenproof dish and cover with a mixture of the breadcrumbs and grated cheese. Bake at 220°C/425°F/Gas 7 for 30 minutes.

Vegetable crumble

4 oz (100 g) canned butter beans
4 oz (100 g) mixed frozen vegetables, cooked
1 tablespoon (15 ml) tomato purée
1 small slice wholemeal bread, crumbled
1 oz (25 g) reduced-fat cheese, thinly grated

Mix the first 3 ingredients together and place in a greased ovenproof dish. Cover with a mixture of the breadcrumbs and grated cheese. Bake in a pre-heated oven at 200°C/400°F/Gas 6 for 30 minutes.

Vegetable and egg bake

3 oz (75 g) canned butter beans
1 small onion, chopped
3 oz (75 g) canned tomatoes
1 diced green pepper
1 tablespoon (15 ml) tomato purée
1 small egg
4 oz (100 g) plain low-fat cottage cheese
ground black pepper

Heat together the first 5 ingredients and put in a greased ovenproof dish. Beat the egg and add to the cottage cheese. Season with the pepper. Place this mixture on top of the bean mixture. Bake at 180°C/350°F/Gas 4 for 30 minutes.

Curried lentils

2 oz (50 g) red lentils
1 tablespoon (15 ml) tomato purée
10 fl oz (300 ml) water
1 teaspoon (5 ml) mild curry paste
1 oz (25 g) long-grain rice

Boil the first 4 ingredients, then simmer gently until the lentils are cooked. Beat well with a wooden spoon, then serve with the boiled rice.

PASTA

Parmesan pasta

2 oz (50 g) pasta shells, tubes or bows
2 oz (50 g) low-fat cream cheese
1 tablespoon (15 ml) skimmed milk
sprinkling oregano
1 tablespoon (15 ml) grated parmesan cheese

Cook the pasta until *al dente*. Purée the cream cheese, the skimmed milk and the oregano and mix with the pasta. Put into an ovenproof dish and sprinkle the parmesan cheese over. Grill until the top starts to turn brown. Serve immediately.

Spaghetti and sardine sauce

2 oz (50 g) wholemeal spaghetti
2 oz (50 g) canned sardines in tomato sauce
7 oz (175 g) canned tomatoes, drained
sprinkling basil

Cook the spaghetti until *al dente*. Chop the sardines and the tomatoes roughly, add the basil and heat gently in a small saucepan. Serve on the cooked spaghetti.

Mushroom cannelloni

3 oz (75 g) chopped mushrooms
2 tablespoons (30 ml) tomato purée
1 small onion, chopped
3 tubes uncooked cannelloni
1 tablespoon (15 ml) sour cream
2 tablespoons (30 ml) skimmed milk
1 oz (25 g) low-fat cream cheese
1 oz (25 g) reduced-fat hard cheese

Mix the mushrooms, purée and chopped onion together. Use to stuff the cannelloni. Purée the sour cream, milk and cream cheese together. Place the cannelloni in a small ovenproof dish, cover with the cheese purée, then finely grate the hard cheese and sprinkle on top of the cheese purée. Bake at 200°C/400°F/Gas 6 for 30 minutes.

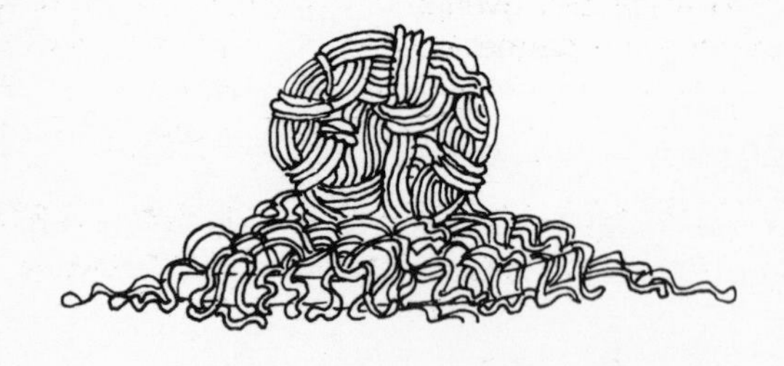

Prawn lasagne

7 oz (175 g) canned tomatoes
1 tablespoon (15 ml) tomato purée
dash chilli sauce
1 teaspoon (5 ml) cornflour
2 sheets (1 oz/50 g) green lasagne
2 oz (50 g) prawns
1 small slice wholemeal bread, crumbled
1 tablespoon (15 ml) grated parmesan cheese

Roughly chop the canned tomatoes and heat gently with the purée and chilli sauce. Mix the cornflour with a little water and add to the mixture. When it thickens, remove from the heat. Spread a little of the sauce over the bottom of a one-person casserole dish. Place one sheet of the lasagne on the sauce, mix half of the remaining sauce with the prawns and place evenly over the lasagne. Cover with the remaining sheet of lasagne, then spoon the remaining sauce over this. Mix the breadcrumbs and cheese together and spoon over the top. Bake at 190°C/375°F/Gas 5 for 35 minutes.

Tagliatelle

2 oz (50 g) tagliatelle
1 oz (25 g) lean ham, trimmed
1 tablespoon (15 ml) cooked peas
1 oz (25 g) low-fat cream cheese
2 tablespoons (30 ml) skimmed milk
1 tablespoon (15 ml) grated parmesan cheese

Cook the tagliatelle until *al dente,* then mix with the chopped ham and peas. Purée the cream cheese and milk. Put the tagliatelle mixture into a greased ovenproof dish, cover with the cheese purée and then the parmesan. Grill until the top starts to turn brown.

Curried beef

2 oz (50 g) brown long-grain rice
2 oz (50 g) lean ground beef
1 tablespoon (15 ml) tomato purée
1 teaspoon (5 ml) mild curry paste

Cook the long-grain rice. Meanwhile, cook the beef in a non-stick pan, stirring continuously. Pour off any fat that appears and then add the purée and curry paste. Heat through until the meat is well cooked. When the rice is ready mix with the meat and serve immediately.

Prawn risotto

2 oz (50 g) brown long-grain rice
10 fl oz (300 ml) chicken stock
2 tablespoons (30 ml) cooked peas
2 oz (50 g) shelled prawns

Cook the rice in the stock for about 30 minutes or until the stock is absorbed and the rice is cooked. Just before the end of the cooking time add the peas and prawns to the saucepan so that they will heat through in the steam. Mix thoroughly before serving.

Chicken risotto

2 oz (50 g) brown long-grain rice
10 fl oz (300 ml) chicken stock
2 oz (50 g) cooked shredded chicken, without skin
1 tablespoon (15 ml) sweetcorn

Cook the rice in the stock until the stock is absorbed and the rice is cooked. Just before the end of the cooking time add the chicken and sweetcorn to let them heat through in the steam. Mix thoroughly before serving.

Vegetable rice

1 small onion, chopped
1 clove of garlic, crushed
1 teaspoon (5 ml) oil
1 teaspoon (5 ml) mild curry paste
2 oz (50 g) cauliflower florets
2 tablespoons (30 ml) frozen peas
1 tablespoon (15 ml) sultanas
2 oz (50 g) brown long-grain rice

Gently heat together the first 4 ingredients. Add the vegetables and sultanas and cook for 1 minute. Then add the rice and 5 fl oz (150 ml) water. Cover tightly and simmer for 15 minutes.

Lentils and rice

1 small onion, chopped
1 teaspoon (5 ml) oil
1 teaspoon (5 ml) curry paste
1 oz (25 g) green lentils, soaked overnight
2 oz (50 g) brown long-grain rice
2 oz (50 g) courgettes
2 oz (50 g) mange-tout

Heat the onion in the oil. Add the curry paste and stir through. Then add the rest of the ingredients and 10 fl oz (300 ml) water. Cook for 20 minutes or until the rice and vegetables are cooked.

Potatoes cowboy-style

1 6-oz (150-g) baked potato in jacket
2 teaspoons (10 ml) low-fat spread
5 oz (125 g) canned barbecue beans

Open the baked potato and spread with low-fat spread. Heat the beans through and serve on top.

Tuna in jacket

1 8-oz (200-g) baked potato in jacket
3 oz (75 g) tuna canned in brine, drained
2 teaspoons (10 ml) low-fat seafood dressing

Open the baked potato and top with the mixed tuna and seafood dressing.

Cheese special

1 8-oz (200-g) baked potato in jacket
1 tablespoon (15 ml) low-fat mayonnaise
1 oz (25 g) reduced-fat hard cheese, grated
ground black pepper

Open the baked potato and serve with the mixed mayonnaise. Sprinkle the cheese on top. Season with black pepper.

Potato omelette

4 oz (100 g) boiled potato
1 egg, beaten
2 tablespoons (30 ml) cooked peas
2 tablespoons (30 ml) sweetcorn
diced red pepper
sprinkling oregano
ground black pepper
1 oz (25 g) reduced-fat hard cheese, grated

Mix all the ingredients except the cheese together, then heat gently in a non-stick pan. Form into an 'omelette'. Sprinkle the cheese on top. Melt the cheese under the grill before serving.

Potato bake

6 oz (150 g) sliced cooked potato
4 oz (100 g) leaf spinach
2 oz (50 g) chopped mushrooms
1 tablespoon (15 ml) tomato purée
1 oz (25 g) reduced-fat hard cheese, grated

Use half of the potato to line a greased ovenproof dish. Chop the spinach roughly and cook for a few minutes until reduced. Mix with the mushrooms, purée and grated cheese, and place on the potato. Top with the rest of the potato. Bake at 200°C/400°F/Gas 6 for 30 minutes.

Open prawn sandwich

1 large slice wholemeal bread
1 teaspoon (5 ml) low-fat spread
few lettuce leaves
3 oz (75 g) shelled prawns
1 tablespoon (15 ml) low-fat seafood dressing

Spread the bread with the low-fat spread, then cover with lettuce leaves. Mix the prawns with the seafood dressing and place on top.

Open tuna sandwich

1 large slice wholemeal bread
1 teaspoon (5 ml) low-fat spread
Chinese leaves
3½ oz (100 g) tuna canned in brine, drained
1 tablespoon (15 ml) low-fat seafood dressing

Spread the bread with the low-fat spread, then top with the Chinese leaves. Mix the tuna and seafood dressing and place on top.

Open chicken sandwich

1 large slice wholemeal bread
1 teaspoon (5 ml) low-fat spread
few slices cucumber
2 oz (50 g) cooked chicken, without skin
1 tablespoon (15 ml) low-fat mayonnaise

Spread the bread with the low-fat spread. Top with the cucumber. Shred the chicken, mix with the mayonnaise and place on top.

Cheese-filled pitta

1 piece pitta bread
1 tablespoon (15 ml) tomato purée
sprinkling oregano
1 oz (25 g) low-fat cream cheese
1 oz (25 g) reduced-fat hard cheese

Spread the pitta with the tomato purée, then sprinkle the oregano on top. Mix the two cheeses together and place on top. Grill until the cheeses start to melt.

Meat-filled pitta

1 piece pitta bread
1 tablespoon (15 ml) tomato purée
1 teaspoon (5 ml) curry paste
1 reduced-fat hamburger
shredded white cabbage
1 carrot, finely grated

Halve the pitta bread. Mix the tomato purée and the curry paste together and coat the hamburger with it. Grill well, then chop and fill the pitta with the meat and vegetables.

SIDE DISHES

Choose two of these side dishes to serve with your main dish. Vegetables are essential to maintaining a good supply of vitamins and nutrients, so ensure that you stay in good health by including some vegetable element in every main meal.

Hot dishes

Baked beans

3½ oz (100 g) sugar-free baked beans

Heat through and serve with a main dish.

Butter beans

2 oz (50 g) canned butter beans
squeeze lemon juice
sprinkling thyme

Heat the butter beans through and season with lemon juice and thyme.

Mixed beans

4 oz (100 g) runner beans
1 oz (25 g) canned broad beans
squeeze lemon juice
ground black pepper

Cook the runner beans until they start to soften. Add the broad beans and allow to heat through. Drain and season with the lemon juice and the pepper.

Green beans

3 oz (75 g) whole green beans
3 oz (75 g) carrots, sliced lengthways
1 teaspoon (5 ml) low-fat spread

Cook the beans and carrots until they start to soften. Drain and add the low-fat spread. Serve immediately.

Broccoli with almonds

3 oz (75 g) broccoli
1 tablespoon (15 ml) flaked almonds
squeeze lemon juice

Cook the broccoli and grill the almonds until they just start to brown. Mix together and season with the lemon juice.

Brussels sprouts

4 oz (100 g) brussels sprouts
1 teaspoon (5 ml) low-fat spread

Cook the brussels sprouts and serve with the low-fat spread.

Green cabbage

4 oz (100 g) green cabbage
1 teaspoon (5 ml) low-fat spread
sprinkling thyme
ground black pepper

Shred the cabbage and cook lightly, drain and add the low-fat spread. Season with the thyme and pepper.

White cabbage and sweetcorn

4 oz (100 g) white cabbage
1 teaspoon (5 ml) low-fat spread
1 tablespoon (15 ml) sweetcorn
squeeze lemon juice

Shred the cabbage and cook lightly, drain and add the low-fat spread and sweetcorn. Heat through, then season with the lemon juice.

Carrots with mustard

4 oz (100 g) sliced carrots
1 teaspoon (5 ml) low-fat spread
1 teaspoon (5 ml) french mustard

Cook the carrots, drain and add the low-fat spread. Season with the mustard.

Carrots with cranberry

4 oz (100 g) sliced carrots
2 teaspoons (10 ml) cranberry sauce
squeeze lemon juice

Cook the carrots, drain and add the cranberry sauce. Heat through gently, then season with the lemon juice.

Cauliflower

6 oz (150 g) cauliflower
1 teaspoon (5 ml) low-fat spread
ground black pepper

Cook the cauliflower, drain and add the low-fat spread. Season with the pepper.

Low-calorie cauliflower cheese

3 oz (75 g) cauliflower
1 tablespoon (15 ml) low-fat natural yoghurt
1 oz (25 g) low-fat cream cheese
ground black pepper

Cook the cauliflower and drain. Purée the yoghurt and cheese together and add to the cauliflower. Heat through gently. Season with the pepper. Serve immediately.

Fennel with tomatoes

3 oz (75 g) fennel
2 canned tomatoes, drained
2 teaspoons (10 ml) grated parmesan cheese

Slice and boil the fennel. Put in an ovenproof dish. Roughly chop the tomatoes and place on top of the fennel. Sprinkle the parmesan cheese over and grill until the top starts to turn brown.

Creamed leeks

1 leek, trimmed and sliced
1 oz (25 g) low-fat cream cheese
1 tablespoon (15 ml) skimmed milk
ground black pepper

Boil the leek until soft. Drain. Purée the cheese and milk and add to the leeks. Heat through, then season with pepper.

Mange-tout

4 oz (100 g) mange-tout
squeeze lemon juice
sprinkling mint

Cook the mange-tout lightly, drain and season with the lemon juice and mint.

Poached mushrooms

4 oz (100 g) button mushrooms
3 fl oz (100 ml) skimmed milk
sprinkling thyme
ground black pepper

Poach the mushrooms in the milk. Drain. Season with the thyme and pepper.

Vegetable mix

7 oz (175 g) canned tomatoes
2 oz (50 g) courgette, sliced
2 oz (50 g) mushrooms, sliced
sprinkling mixed herbs
1 teaspoon (5 ml) cornflour

Roughly chop the tomatoes, then sweat the vegetables together over a low heat in a non-stick pan. Season with the herbs. Mix the cornflour with a little water and add to the vegetable mix. Continue to heat until the sauce thickens.

Tomatoes and mushrooms

2 canned tomatoes
2 oz (50 g) mushrooms, sliced
1 tablespoon (15 ml) tomato purée
sprinkling oregano
1 clove garlic, crushed

Roughly chop the tomatoes, then gently heat through all the ingredients.

Parsnips

2 oz (50 g) parsnips, sliced
1 tablespoon (15 ml) peas
1 teaspoon (5 ml) low-fat spread
ground black pepper

Cook the parsnips and peas. Drain. Add the low-fat spread and season with pepper.

Peas

3 tablespoons (45 ml) cooked peas
1 tablespoon (15 ml) sweetcorn
squeeze lemon juice
sprinkling mint

Heat the peas and corn gently. Season with the lemon juice and mint.

Peppers

2 oz (50 g) mixed diced peppers
1 tablespoon (15 ml) cooked peas
1 teaspoon (5 ml) oil
dash soy sauce

Quickly stir-fry the peppers and peas in the oil. Season with the soy sauce.

Mushrooms in oyster sauce

4 oz (100 g) mushrooms, sliced
2 tablespoons (30 ml) oyster sauce

Quickly heat the mushrooms and the sauce together.

Spiced mushrooms

4 oz (100 g) mushrooms, sliced
1 tablespoon (15 ml) cooked peas
1 teaspoon (5 ml) mild curry paste

Quickly stir-fry all the ingredients together.

Spiced pumpkin

3 oz (75 g) pumpkin flesh, cubed
1 tablespoon (15 ml) raisins
1 teaspoon (5 ml) mild curry paste

Sweat the pumpkin in a non-stick pan until soft, then add the other ingredients and quickly stir-fry.

Curried spinach with mushrooms

3 oz (75 g) leaf spinach
2 oz (50 g) mushrooms, chopped
1 tablespoon (15 ml) tomato purée
1 teaspoon (5 ml) mild curry paste

Shred the spinach, then cook for a few minutes until reduced, add the rest of the ingredients and quickly heat through.

Spinach

4 oz (100 g) leaf spinach
1 teaspoon (5 ml) low-fat spread
ground black pepper

Shred the spinach, then cook for a few minutes until reduced. Add the low-fat spread, then season with the pepper.

Swede and carrot

3 oz (75 g) cooked swede
3 oz (75 g) cooked carrot
1 teaspoon (5 ml) low-fat spread
1 tablespoon (15 ml) skimmed milk
ground black pepper

Mash together all the ingredients and serve immediately.

Turnip

5 oz (125 g) cooked turnip, sliced
1 teaspoon (5 ml) low-fat spread
1 teaspoon (5 ml) brown sugar

Heat the turnip slices in a non-stick pan, then add the low-fat spread and the sugar and raise the heat until a glaze forms. Mix well and serve immediately.

Cold beans

3 oz (75 g) cooked whole green beans
1 teaspoon (5 ml) poppy seeds
1 tablespoon (15 ml) oil-free french dressing

Mix all the ingredients together.

Courgettes and peas

2 oz (50 g) courgette, grated
2 tablespoons (30 ml) cooked peas
squeeze lemon juice
ground black pepper

Mix all the ingredients together.

Minty mixture

2 oz (50 g) courgette, grated
1 tablespoon (15 ml) cooked peas
1 tablespoon (15 ml) low-fat natural yoghurt
1 teaspoon (5 ml) mint sauce

Mix all the ingredients together.

Curry mix

2 oz (50 g) courgette, grated
2 oz (50 g) carrot, grated
1 tablespoon (15 ml) low-fat natural yoghurt
1 teaspoon (5 ml) mild curry paste

Mix all the ingredients together.

Carrot and sweetcorn

2 oz (50 g) carrot
1 tablespoon (15 ml) sweetcorn
1 teaspoon (5 ml) poppy seeds
1 tablespoon (15 ml) oil-free french dressing

Mix all the ingredients together.

Grated carrot salad

2 oz (50 g) carrot, grated
1 tablespoon (15 ml) low-calorie mayonnaise
ground black pepper

Mix all the ingredients together.

Dressed carrot and sweetcorn

2 oz (50 g) carrot, grated
1 tablespoon (15 ml) sweetcorn
1 tablespoon (15 ml) low-calorie seafood dressing

Mix all the ingredients together.

Minted cabbage

2 oz (50 g) white cabbage, grated
1 tablespoon (15 ml) cooked peas
1 tablespoon (15 ml) low-fat natural yoghurt
squeeze lemon juice
1 teaspoon (5 ml) mint sauce

Mix all the ingredients together.

Curried cabbage salad

2 oz (50 g) white cabbage, grated
2 oz (50 g) carrot, grated
1 tablespoon (15 ml) low-fat natural yoghurt
squeeze lemon juice
1 teaspoon (5 ml) mild curry paste

Mix all the ingredients together.

Mixed cabbage salad

2 oz (50 g) white cabbage, grated
2 oz (50 g) red cabbage, grated
1 teaspoon (5 ml) poppy seeds
1 tablespoon (15 ml) orange juice
1 tablespoon (15 ml) oil-free french dressing

Mix all the ingredients together.

Mushroom salad

4 oz (100 g) cold poached mushrooms
1 tablespoon (15 ml) red wine vinegar
1 teaspoon (5 ml) poppy seeds
1 tablespoon (15 ml) oil-free french dressing

Mix all the ingredients together. Chill.

French tomato salad

2 tomatoes, sliced
½ small onion, sliced
1 teaspoon (5 ml) poppy seeds
1 tablespoon (15 ml) oil-free french dressing

Mix all the ingredients together. Chill.

Cold cauliflower

4 oz (100 g) cold cooked cauliflower
squeeze lemon juice
sprinkling mixed herbs
1 tablespoon (15 ml) oil-free french dressing

Mix all the ingredients together.Chill.

Peas and sweetcorn

2 tablespoons (30 ml) cooked peas
1 tablespoon (15 ml) sweetcorn
1 tablespoon (15 ml) oil-free french dressing
sprinkling mint

Mix all the ingredients together.Chill.

Mixed salad

lettuce
cucumber, sliced
celery, chopped
sprinkling mixed herbs
2 tablespoons (30 ml) oil-free french dressing

Mix the salad ingredients together and dress with the herbs and oil-free french dressing.

Grapefruit salad

Chinese leaves
chicory
3 oz (75 g) canned grapefruit in natural juice
1 tablespoon (15 ml) low-fat natural yoghurt
squeeze lemon juice

Mix all the ingredients together.

Lemon-dressed sweetcorn and peas

1 tablespoon (15 ml) sweetcorn
1 tablespoon (15 ml) cooked peas
celerey, chopped
1 tablespoon (15 ml) low-fat natural yoghurt
squeeze lemon juice
ground black pepper

Mix all the ingredients together.

Peas and thyme

lettuce
watercress
2 tablespoons (30 ml) cooked peas
sprinkling thyme
2 tablespoons (30 ml) oil-free french dressing

Mix the salad ingredients together. Dress with the herb and oil-free french dressing.

Basil tomatoes

2 tomatoes, sliced
1 clove garlic, crushed
sprinkling basil
1 tablespoon (15 ml) low-calorie seafood dressing
squeeze lemon juice

Mix all the ingredients together.

Artichoke salad

lettuce
curly endive
3 oz (75 g) canned artichoke hearts
sprinkling mint
2 tablespoons (30 ml) oil-free french dressing

Mix all the ingredients together.

Peas and artichoke

Chinese leaves
1 tablespoon (15 ml) cooked peas
3 oz (75 g) canned artichoke hearts
squeeze lemon juice
1 tablespoon (15 ml) low-fat natural yoghurt
ground black pepper

Mix all the ingredients together.

Cucumber and kiwi salad

curly endive
diced cucumber
½ kiwi fruit, sliced
1 tablespoon (15 ml) low-fat natural yoghurt
squeeze lemon juice

Mix all the ingredients together.

Cheese-dressed salad

chicory
watercress
diced cucumber
1 oz (25 g) low-fat cream cheese
1 tablespoon (15 ml) skimmed milk
squeeze lemon juice

Mix the salad ingredients together. Purée the rest of the ingredients. Dress the salad with this mixture.

Dressed fruit salad

diced melon
seedless grapes
hulled strawberries
1 oz (25 g) low-fat cream cheese
2 tablespoons (30 ml) skimmed milk

Mix the fruits together. Purée the cheese and milk and dress the fruits with this mixture.

Orange-dressed cabbage

1 oz (25 g) red cabbage, shredded
1 oz (25 g) carrot, shredded
watercress
1 teaspoon (5 ml) raisins
1 tablespoon (15 ml) oil-free french dressing
1 tablespoon (15 ml) orange juice

Mix the salad ingredients together, then mix the french dressing and orange juice together and dress the salad with this mixture.

Chinese salad

2 oz (50 g) bamboo shoots
sliced red pepper
2 oz (50 g) mushrooms, sliced
dash soy sauce
1 tablespoon (15 ml) oil-free french dressing

Mix the salad ingredients together, then mix the soy sauce and french dressing together and dress the salad with this mixture.

Minted green salad

Chinese leaves
sliced green pepper
sliced celery
1 tablespoon (15 ml) low-calorie mayonnaise
1 tablespoon (15 ml) skimmed milk
1 teaspoon (5 ml) mint sauce

Mix the salad ingredients together. Mix the rest of the ingredients together and dress the salad with this mixture.

Leeks and peas

2 oz (50 g) leeks, shredded finely
1 tablespoon (15 ml) cooked peas
1 tablespoon (15 ml) low-fat blue-cheese dressing
1 tablespoon (15 ml) skimmed milk

Mix the leeks and peas together, then mix together the blue-cheese dressing and the milk and dress the salad with this mixture.

Eating out

Few of us are now at home all day every day, able to control exactly what we eat at each meal. Whether because we work away from home or we go out to eat for social reasons, most of us eat at least a proportion of our food outside the home, and this may well contain ingredients not apparent to the eye that increase the calorie count of each item. For this reason, the best ploy is to opt for the simplest food that you can – a piece of meat without sauce, plus a salad, for example, or if you know that you are going to be away from home at lunchtime, take a teaspoon with you and settle down with a small carton of cottage cheese, a small wholemeal roll and a piece of fruit.

If you have to eat more than you had intended to at lunchtime, make that your main meal of the day and have only a light meal that evening. If you are really dining in style, count some of the meal in your Cheat Unit quota for the week so that your over-indulgence is kept in check.

Try never to get into the position where you are so hungry that you wolf down a low-fibre, high-fat snack that uses up your lunch allowance without actually filling you up – you'll regret it bitterly later. And do make sure that you enjoy your food. Don't let yourself go through lunch without noticing what you are eating: concentrate on the activity of eating. Have water or a low-calorie drink with it as well: this will reduce your appetite and make you feel fuller sooner. If you are dining out, make the most of it as a social occasion. My maxim is to eat slowly, talk a lot, and leave a little. Then, as long as you are enthusiastic about the meal, no one will guess that you are on a diet.

This section provides ground rules for eating out in a variety of situations – from Sunday tea with the in-laws to lunch at the works canteen, to the hidden calorie traps in various types of restaurant.

Canteens

These vary a great deal – so much so that generalizations are very difficult. Some provide no choice of meal, and if it is a stodgy, calorie-laden or otherwise unappetizing one there may be no alternative other than to go out and buy yourself some fast food, and in future pack yourself a salad or a sandwich to bring in to work. At many canteens nowadays, however, there is a daily choice of several dishes, including vegetarian ones, and salads are usually available.

The items to avoid on canteen menus are specifically the fried foods – especially chips – and anything in a thick gravy or sauce. Cheese, too (other than cottage cheese), is probably best avoided.

Here are some possibilities for the dieter chosen from standard canteen fare:

(1) soup with an unbuttered wholemeal roll;
(2) jacket potato (without fat) with vegetables or salad;
(3) cottage cheese, lean beef or ham, prawn, chicken without skin, or tuna salad (avoid salads to which mayonnaise or french dressing has already been added);
(4) any grilled, braised or casseroled meats with vegetables – but without potatoes, pasta or rice;
(5) any grilled or poached fish that is not in sauce, with a small quantity of vegetables and boiled potatoes, rice or pasta.

Eating with friends or relatives

General advice is the same: avoid the gravies and sauces, keep a strict eye on the number of potatoes, or amount of rice or pasta, you eat, but fill up on vegetables – if you have several helpings of these no one will notice that you've been pretty abstemious with the rest.

You may think this is all very well except in the case of the Sunday lunch with relatives: there's something about The Roast that makes people very defensive, and everyone seems to think that their mother/spouse makes the best ever tasted. The answer is to tread even more carefully than usual. Don't forget the principle of eating slowly, talking a lot and leaving a little. Refuse the gravy if you get a chance to, because it will have been made with fat from the meat. Surreptitiously cut off any fat you can see on the meat, exclaim how wonderful the roast potatoes are (then eat only one and leave the rest), and when urged to a second helping go for the vegetables.

Declare how marvellous the meal was before anyone else has finished their main course. Then ask if you can lie down, as you're not used to eating so much – having done so, you can promptly feign sleep so that you don't have to face the dessert. If none of these ploys works and you find yourself sinning shamelessly, the only solution is to drag everyone out for a ten-mile walk. This will ensure firstly that you work off some of the damage inflicted by the meal and secondly that you are never invited again.

Another hallowed gastronomic occasion is Sunday tea – a great moment of pride, usually, for whoever produced this stunning array of calories. Summon up as much willpower as you can, take only a little and proclaim loudly how delicious it all is. *In extremis* invent an allergy to chocolate or cream.

Picnics

These usually fall into one or two categories: knife-and-fork affairs or spreads comprised of little bite-sized mouthfuls that you can pick up between the fingers – and hence tend to keep picking at as long as the food remains on show. If you are masterminding the menu yourself, you can of course ensure that the fare offered will suit your own slimline requirements. Here are some calorie- conscious possibilities to prepare for picnics.

For the held-in-the-hand picnic spread:

(1) sandwiches made with low-fat spread and low-fat fillings such as turkey, chicken, lean beef or ham, low-fat cheese, tuna in brine, drained and mixed with a low-fat dressing; pad out with lettuce, grated carrot, etc.; cut into quarters and wrap each individually in clingfilm – and don't then get carried away and eat too many;

(2) boned chicken breasts, without skin, well seasoned with pepper and soy sauce, grilled, left to cool and cut into bite-sized pieces;

(3) vegetable crudités (carrots, pepper, cucumber, cauliflower, baby sweetcorn), wrapped in clingfilm to ensure freshness, served with low-fat or oil-free salad dressings in little bowls;

(4) bite-sized pieces of fresh fruit.

If your picnic is a knife-and-fork affair, try some of the following:

(1) slices of lean beef and ham, sliced low-fat hard cheese, smoked salmon, chicken pieces (grilled well without skin);
(2) bean salad made from a variety of canned beans, dressed with herbs and oil-free french dressing;
(3) coleslaw made with grated white cabbage and carrot and dressed with low-calorie dressing;
(4) small cooked new potatoes or rice salad made with brown long-grain rice and cooked peas, dressed with herbs and oil-free french dressing.

For picnic drinks you really can't beat the low-alcohol wines that are now on the market. These are light and fresh, which make them ideal for a picnic. Do try to keep them cool – you can now get drawstring cool bags that you carry over your shoulder. The other great advantage of these wines is that there will be no problem with drinking and driving. Take some lager too and some non-alcoholic drink, such as mineral water.

Fast-food shops and restaurants

The proliferation of fast-food outlets in recent years has made life much easier for both people at work and shoppers who can't get back home for lunch. The discerning dieter now has a considerable choice in many areas, which is a great boon if your place of work has no canteen – or a bad one.

The best fast-food outlet that you can patronize is a sandwich bar where your sandwich is made to order. If there were more of these around there would also be a lot more satisfied dieters. If you don't have access to a sandwich bar, you could try sandwiches from one of the big food chains. However, whichever filling you go for you will inevitably end up with more than you bargained for in the form of butter or dressings.

If you have the time to stop and sit down or are meeting a friend for lunch, try a coffee shop or tea house. Here you can have a soup with wholemeal roll (unbuttered) or a ham or prawn salad. Some now offer jacket potatoes, which, topped with prawns or cottage cheese (do not add fat if you are trying to lose weight), make a substantial lunch. But beware. In these places you are often confronted with piles of delicious-looking cakes, so you'll have to use considerable willpower to resist them.

If time is very short and you are eating on the run, do not despair. Although it is something that I would not recommend you to have very often, there is no harm in the occasional hamburger, but accompanied only by a drink (coffee or diet coke) – no chips, no relish, no bun.

Fish and chip shops and fried-chicken take-aways aren't a good idea for slimmers, because the fish and the chicken are always deep-fried, often in batter (extremely fattening), and the chips, also oil-sodden, are disastrous. Avoid these places like the plague.

Your main choices when eating out at lunchtime are therefore:

(1) sandwich bar: choose brown bread, no butter, then chicken, turkey, cottage cheese, prawn, lean roast beef or ham, tuna – but no dressing: pad out with some salad stuff;
(2) sit-down meal with soup and a wholemeal roll, a ham or prawn salad, or a jacket potato (without fat) topped with cottage cheese, prawns or baked beans;
(3) small hamburger and coffee or diet coke.

Restaurants

If you want to play safe (maybe you are nearing your goal weight and do not want to be deterred by anything, even a slap-up dinner), opt for a restaurant in one of the big chains. These always offer good value for money and owing to the strict portion control you can be assured that you will not be going too far astray. However, every time you walk into a little French bistro or Italian trattoria you will be playing with fire and almost certainly the sinner in you will win out.

One of the most important factors in your strategy will be how often you eat out. If you rarely do so unless it is a very special occasion, you would be foolish to let the thought of your diet ruin your night out. Forget it entirely and go to town, satisfy any unrequited urges that you have been feeling and just enjoy yourself – after all, that is the whole idea of going out to celebrate. Then put your splurge behind you and carry on eating normally the next day. Don't even try to make up those extra Cheat Units. You may not lose any weight that week, but wasn't it worth it just for once?

If on the other hand you are a regular socialite and eat out every week or so, or several times a week, you cannot afford to take this view. You must control what you consume. Contrary to popular belief, it is not necessary to consume large quantities of food in restaurants in order to put weight on: it is *what* you eat that really matters. Unfortunately most restaurants do not yet give people much choice of low-fat alternatives, such as low-calorie mayonnaise, oil-free dressing or low-fat spreads, but the time must surely come when this is the custom. If, meanwhile, you are brave enough to request such items when you eat out you will be bringing that day a little nearer. Otherwise, think very carefully before placing your order.

BRITISH RESTAURANTS

Among the most popular traditional British restaurants are carveries where you can take the family for Sunday lunch. These are good places for slimmers, as you can generally serve yourself. When you do so, concentrate on the vegetables, take just a little meat and remove all visible fat from it before you eat it. Limit yourself to *one* roast potato. Ensure you won't be able to face a dessert by making sure you eat a great quantity of vegetables. As a starter opt for something light such as melon or grapefruit, a fruit juice or a light soup such as consommé or cock-a-leekie. If this really is a rare treat for you, go ahead and have what you want – even a prawn cocktail, if that is what you crave, but no bread and butter.

If you must have a dessert, opt for a fresh fruit sorbet or a small portion of ice cream. Again, if this is a special treat then be a little less strict with yourself and have a crême caramel or *small* portion of cheesecake, but no added cream.

Steak houses are the dieter's dream. Go for the smallest

rump, sirloin or fillet steak, well grilled and served with an undressed salad and jacket potato, and you will have no problem. Use your Cheat Units, if you wish, to indulge in a glass or two of wine with your meal.

If, on the other hand, you go to a fish restaurant, you could opt for smoked salmon or trout as a starter, or even oysters (which, though expensive, are not fattening). For the main course the choice available will probably include Dover sole, salmon, trout and fresh crab, any of which would be suitable if served without sauce and dressing.

At other restaurants you may be offered braised kidneys (which are suitable for slimmers as long as they do not come in a rich sauce) or a piece of gammon. Again, remember to remove any visible fat. As well as sorbets and ice creams for desserts there will probably be a fresh fruit salad and possibly, in season, summer pudding – a treat only a martyr could resist.

Whatever the menu you settle on, do remember not to indulge in too much alcohol and to refuse any rolls or bread and butter that comes your way. Try to eat lightly during the rest of the day. Assume that the meal will absorb that day's Cheat Units and revert the next day to your usual regime.

FRENCH RESTAURANTS

These are decidedly more dangerous ground for slimmers but can still be safe if you choose wisely. For a starter you may find consommé on the menu. There will almost certainly be some crudités, which although sometimes more fattening than the home-made variety are still a feasible choice; be wary of the dip, however, and limit your consumption of it as far as possible. *Moules marinières* might be permissible as a special treat. If you really can't see anything that you think would be safe, that is, something that is not brimming with oil, butter or cream, miss out the starter and treat yourself to another drink, having one mouthful of your companion's starter (don't forget, however, that pure fruit juice – tomato, orange or grapefruit, for example – makes a good low-calorie starter).

You may be able to have a grilled or poached fish as your

main course, otherwise opt for *steak au poivre* (pepper steak) or a casseroled beef dish such as *boeuf carbonnade* or *bourguignonne*. Go easy on the side vegetables here as they will probably contain added butter, and ignore any potato dish entirely. A few mouthfuls of boiled rice would be the best option.

For dessert, choose fresh fruit or a sorbet, steadfastly ignoring the wonderful tarts and gâteaux you will be offered from the sweet trolley. These melt-in-the-mouth confections will *not* melt away your waistline.

ITALIAN RESTAURANTS

These too are veritable minefields for anyone on a diet, and you must know how to pick your way through the menu if you are to emerge unscathed.

If melon is on offer it will probably be your wisest choice of starter. If you really must be more adventurous go for melon and parma ham. Otherwise, treat yourself to fruit juice or another drink instead of a starter.

You may be able to have a simple grilled steak, but you will be unlikely to find a chicken dish that is not smothered in cream, cheese or chopped into small pieces and fried in olive oil. A starter-sized portion of pasta may be available as a main course, but don't bank on it: it will still be fairly fattening, but will probably make you feel full enough not to crave a dessert. Otherwise, have the plainest main course available, with an undressed side salad or plain vegetables. Refuse the potato. If you must have a dessert, the best choice will again be fresh fruit or sorbet. If you go for ice cream, beware the more complicated calorie-laden concoctions often listed in Italian menus, such as cassata.

If you go to a pizza house, order a side salad with your pizza (again, no dressing on the salad) and give some of your pizza to your companion.

CHINESE RESTAURANTS

You will probably be sharing a set meal with others at a Chinese restaurant, so make the most of your chance to eat sparingly by letting your friends have the lion's share.

Choose plain boiled rather than fried rice. Avoid the spareribs, which are loaded with fat, and the sweet-and-sour dishes. Among your best bets would be Peking duck and a dish based on beansprouts, which are very filling without being too fattening. Be sure to eat with chopsticks, too, so that you do not get through your meal too fast.

Ignore the sweet course completely, although if others are indulging you might allow yourself a lychee from someone else's dish!

Lastly, never go to a Chinese restaurant when you are starving, or you will certainly regret it when you next step on the scales.

INDIAN RESTAURANTS

Again, you will probably be sharing these dishes with other people. Good! Let them do most of the eating. Indian food is not generally designed to help people lose weight, owing to the curry sauces, which often have a high fat content. Skip the starter and try to pick a sensible main dish. Tandoori chicken is your best choice. Take your time eating it, and eat all of the salad garnish. With luck the others will have polished off the rest by the time you have finished. Any other selection will undo days of good behaviour – and any Indian dessert is absolutely lethal, so avoid these at all costs.

GREEK RESTAURANTS

If you are eating with friends, persuade them to opt for *meze* – a dazzling succession of small dishes that you can pick from delicately while allowing your friends to demolish the rest.

Otherwise, avoid the starters, as most of them will be extremely fattening, especially *taramasalata* and *houmus,* which may contain more calories than most main courses.

If red mullet are on the menu choose these. Your next safest bet would be *dolmades* (stuffed vine leaves) or *souvlakia* (kebabs). Fill up on a plain side salad, but remember not to let any dressing near it. All Greek desserts are incredibly fattening, so never be tempted even to think about them, and avoid the Greek coffee too, which often comes ready-sugared.

MEXICAN RESTAURANTS

Unfortunately Mexican food, too, is often calorie-crammed. It is wise to ignore the starters. Those innocent-looking corn chips are incredibly high in carlories. The only feasible main course is tacos, but remember that cheese, sour cream and avocados, the trimmings that often accompany Mexican dishes, are all high in calories.

You may be able to get a sorbet for dessert. If, however, the choice is between cheesecake, chocolate mousse and the like, forget it!

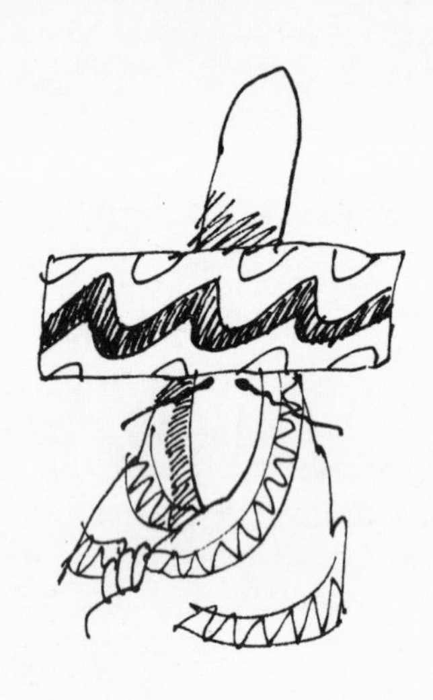

PUBS AND WINE BARS

Many pubs have now gone for catering in a big way. Along with their upmarket cousins, the wine bars, they offer a potential hazard to the would-be dieter. One item that would certainly bring about your downfall is the ploughman's lunch. Don't even think about it. A beef, ham or chicken sandwich is a much safer bet – without dressing.

Pâté, quiche and smoked mackerel – standard wine-bar fare – are all fattening, but you could have a *small* slice of quiche with an undressed salad as an evening meal (don't have it for lunch unless you are planning a very light evening meal).

If you must have something hot, opt for a bowl of soup and a roll, or even a small hamburger. Jacket potatoes are also a fairly safe bet if you don't have butter with them.

All in all, though it is not impossible to eat out and keep to your diet, it is obviously easier to eat sensibly (in terms of your diet) at certain types of restaurant or hostelry rather than others. Bear this in mind when you are trying to decide where to have your next meal out.

5 Entertaining Ideas

Anyone who really wants to change his or her eating habits will find it safer to entertain at home rather than to eat out with friends. You can enjoy a wider range of dishes at home because you can resort to low-calorie ingredients that as yet are not widely used in restaurant dishes. Also, since it is you that is doing the cooking you can control your menus, and are therefore less likely to go overboard with calorie-laden dishes.

In my opinion there is no better way to spend an evening than sitting down with friends for a good meal, interesting talk and a few glasses of good wine. Although I do not always serve low-calorie dishes to my guests, I *do* try to think of their health as well as my waistline. That is how the dishes in this chapter were born.

Unless it is just a simple meal for friends, my entertaining generally revolves round a theme, perhaps one suggested by the occasion. This chapter is therefore divided accordingly – first, a section on cooking for friends, then one on different national themes, e.g. French, Chinese, Mexican and so on, followed by a section comprising my favourite recipes for occasions such as Guy Fawkes' Night and Valentine's Day.

If you opt for these menus, you should assume that they will use up that day's quota of Cheat Units.

Food for friends

The wide choice of exotic fruit and vegetables and new, leaner cuts of meat, together with the low-fat alternatives to traditionally fatty foods, now available means you can easily create healthy, gourmet dinners for your friends, whether you are planning a quiet dinner for two or an informal get-together for four to eight people.

Meals for two

MENU 1

Fresh asparagus

Fillet steak tournedos
Creamy mustard sauce
Puréed spinach
Julienne carrots

Brandy and chocolate mousse

Asparagus

Trim the woody end, then stand upright in a pan of boiling water and cook for 10-15 minutes until tender. Serve with a sprinkling of fresh mixed herbs or a small pat of low-fat spread.

Fillet steak tournedos

Buy two tournedos from your butcher (some of the big supermarket chains also stock these now), then prepare by brushing with a little low-fat spread and sprinkling with ground black pepper. Grill until well done.

Creamy mustard sauce

Mix 2 fl oz (50 ml) sour cream or single cream substitute with 2 oz (50 g) chopped mushrooms which have been dry-fried in a non-stick pan with 2 teaspoons (10 ml) french mustard. When well mixed gently heat through and serve, placing the tournedos in the middle of each lake of sauce.

Puréed spinach

Cook 8 oz (200 g) shredded leaf spinach, from which all woody stems have been removed, until reduced. Then purée in a blender with 1 teaspoon (5 ml) low-fat spread and a little skimmed milk. Serve with the tournedos.

Julienne carrots

Slice 4 oz (100 g) young carrots thinly lengthwise. Boil until tender. Serve with the tournedos.

Brandy and chocolate mousse

Melt 2 oz (50 g) plain chocolate in a bowl over hot water, then cool slightly. Separate two eggs, beat the yolks and add to the chocolate. Add 1 tablespoon (15 ml) brandy. Whisk the egg whites, then fold gently into the mixture. Divide the mixture between two ramekin dishes. Chill until set.

MENU 2

Creamy tuna pâté

Chicken with red sauce
Baked mushrooms
Peas and leeks

Crispy cocktail fruits

Creamy tuna pâté

Mash a 4-oz (100-g) can of tuna in brine (drained) with some lemon juice and ground black pepper. Beat in 2 tablespoons (30 ml) low-fat yoghurt, 2 oz (50 g) skimmed milk cheese and a chopped garlic clove. Divide between two ramekin dishes. Chill.

Chicken with red sauce

Take two skinned and boned chicken breasts and place in a piece of foil. Blend 1 tablespoon (15 ml) tomato purée with 2 tablespoons (30 ml) red wine and a touch of Worcestershire sauce. Cover the chicken with the sauce, then wrap in the foil. Cook at 200°C/400° F/Gas 6 for 1 hour or until cooked.

Baked mushrooms

Allow 2-3 mushrooms each, depending on size. Top with a little low-fat spread and a few mixed herbs. Bake for 10 minutes. Serve with the chicken.

Peas and leeks

Thinly slice a cleaned leek then boil with 4 oz (100 g) frozen peas until the peas are cooked. Serve with a squeeze of lemon juice and some ground black pepper.

Crispy cocktail fruits

Fill two small meringue cases (from a baker's) with diced fresh fruits or soft summer fruits which have been soaked in a little liquor of your choice.

MENU 3

Spinach soup

Mushroom stroganoff
Tagliatelle

Almond ice cream

Spinach soup

In a non-stick frying-pan, fry a small onion and a crushed clove of garlic in 1 teaspoon (5 ml) oil. Add 8 oz (200 g) shredded spinach and quickly stir-fry. Add this mixture to 10 fl oz (300 ml) apple juice with some ground black pepper, a sprinkling of mixed herbs and some soy sauce. Bring to the boil, then simmer gently for 15-20 minutes until cooked. Liquidize, then add 2 tablespoons (30 ml) low-fat yoghurt. Gently re-heat.

Mushroom stroganoff

Fry a small onion, half a green pepper and 8 oz (200 g) mushrooms in 1 tablespoon (15 ml) olive oil. Add 1 tablespoon (15 ml) wholemeal flour and cook for 1 minute. Add 1 tablespoon (15 ml) red wine and 4 fl oz (120 ml) soured cream or single cream substitute and 1 tablespoon (15 ml) brandy. Heat through and serve on a bed of tagliatelle. Allow 1-2 oz (50-75 g) uncooked weight per person.

Almond ice cream

Mix 4 oz (100 g) plain ice cream with a sprinkling of both ground almonds and flaked almonds. Divide between two dishes and serve each with an almond biscuit.

MENU 4

This is an old but still much-loved recipe. All you need is two people, a bottle of champagne and romantic candlelight . . .

This is the most slimming recipe I know of for two!

Feeding the small crowd

I define a small crowd as anything from four to eight people. When eating with friends, unless there is some theme or special occasion to celebrate, I tend to take a casual, informal approach to entertaining. Your friends come for your company, not to be impressed by you. Some simple, tasty food, a relaxed atmosphere and your own congenial company should make for a successful evening.

These recipes are very elastic and easy to adjust for a greater (or smaller) number of people. Don't forget that you can provide more bread, rice or pasta for people who are not slimming, whilst you stick to what you think is a sensible amount with these foods.

MENU 1

Crudités

Mushroom-stuffed parcels with red wine sauce
Mange-tout
New potatoes

Iced raspberries

Crudités

Trim and slice or divide into bite-sized portions a selection of vegetables such as cauliflower, peppers, cucumber, celery, dwarf corn, carrots. Make a dip from low-calorie mayonnaise, low-fat yoghurt and crushed garlic. Arrange the crudités round the dip and chill before serving.

Mushroom-stuffed parcels

Roughly chop 12 oz (300 g) mushrooms, then fry in a non-stick frying-pan with 1 oz (25 g) butter. When soft, add 2 tablespoons (30 ml) sherry and continue to cook until all moisture has evaporated. Season with black pepper and leave to chill. Take 4-6 large cabbage leaves (depending on number of guests) and divide the mushroom mixture between the leaves. Roll each leaf up into a small parcel and place in a large saucepan with a tight-fitting lid. Add 5 fl oz (150 ml) red wine and 15 fl oz (450 ml) stock. Bring to the boil, then simmer gently for 40-50 minutes or until the cabbage is cooked through. Remove the cabbage rolls and keep warm, add a little cornflour mixed with water to the remaining liquid, then 1 tablespoon (15 ml) tomato purée. Stir until the sauce has slightly thickened. Spoon the sauce on to each plate, then arrange the cabbage parcels, mange-tout and new potatoes on top of the sauce.

Mange-tout

If frozen, cook as directed on packet. If fresh, cook in boiling water until the pods lose their stiffness.

New potatoes

Allow 2 oz (50 g) for yourself and 4 oz (100 g) each for your guests. Cook unpeeled in boiling water until tender.

Iced raspberries

Allow 2 oz (50 g) raspberries per person, purée, then mix with 1 tablespoon (15 ml) whipped double cream substitute per person. Freeze until ready to serve. Serve garnished with whole raspberries and sliced kiwi fruit.

MENU 2

Seafood dip

Goulash
Braised celery and tomatoes
Pasta shells

Strawberry and kiwi cheesecake

Seafood dip

Make a dip out of low-fat yoghurt, low-calorie Thousand Island dressing and a little lemon juice. Arrange round it some crab sticks (defrosted) and unshelled prawns, interspersed with sliced green pepper and cucumber. Serve chilled.

Goulash

Allow about 4 oz (100 g) lean braising beef per person. Cut the meat up into small bite-sized chunks. Chop 1-2 large onions and put with the meat in a slow-cooker or a large casserole dish. Add 2 tablespoons (30 ml) tomato purée, a sprinkling of mixed herbs and 1 tablespoon (15 ml) paprika. Add 10 fl oz (300 ml) beef stock and add to the pot. Either cook for 8-10 hours in the slow-cooker or bring to the boil then simmer gently on a low heat for 2 hours or until the meat is tender. Spoon in a few tablespoonsful of low-fat yoghurt before serving.

Pasta shells

Allow 1 oz (25 g) uncooked weight for yourself and 2-3 oz (50-75 g) each for everyone else. Boil until *al dente*.

Braised celery and tomatoes

Allow 4 oz (100 g) celery per person. Roughly chop, then quickly stir-fry in a non-stick pan with 1 tablespoon (15 ml) oil. Put into a casserole dish with a little stock, cook for 10 minutes or until tender. Add 15 oz (375 g) canned tomatoes (drained and chopped) and 1 tablespoon (15 ml) tomato purée. Cook for a few minutes before serving.

Strawberry and kiwi cheesecake

Crush 4 digestive biscuits, mix with 1 oz (25 g) melted butter and line a small flan dish with the crumbs. Chill until firm. Heat 5 fl oz (150 ml) water and add half a packet of strawberry jelly. Stir until dissolved. Leave to cool, then add 1 tablespoon (15 ml) lemon juice and the grated rind of a lemon. Sieve 8 oz (200 g) cottage cheese and add to the mixture. Mix well, then spread over the base. Chill in the refrigerator until set. Decorate the top with slices of strawberries and kiwi fruit.

MENU 3

Fish bowl

Stuffed chicken breasts
Beans provençal
New potatoes

Strawberry sorbet

Fish bowl

Put some shredded lettuce and watercress in a soup bowl. Arrange on top some oddments of smoked salmon, some sour cream topped with a little red cod's roe, a couple of unshelled prawns and a crab's claw. Garnish with a wedge of lemon.

Stuffed chicken breasts

Allow one boned and skinned chicken breast per person. Flatten, then mix some chopped mushrooms with some low-fat herb cheese and use this to stuff the chicken breasts. Secure the stuffing with some cocktail sticks. Then wrap in foil and bake at 200° C/400°F/Gas 6 for 45 minutes or until the chicken is cooked.

Make the brandy sauce by mixing some single cream substitute with 1 tablespoon (15 ml) brandy and 2 teaspoons (10 ml) french mustard. Mix well, then heat gently and serve each chicken breast with a little of the sauce poured over.

Beans provençal

Allow 2 oz (50 g) fresh french beans per person. Trim, then cook for a few minutes in boiling water until *al dente*. In a non-stick pan heat 1 tablespoon (15 ml) olive oil, add some chopped, drained tomatoes (from a can) and quickly stir-fry. Add the beans and heat through.

New potatoes

Allow 2 oz (50 g) for yourself and 4 oz (100 g) for each guest. Cook unpeeled in boiling water until tender.

Strawberry sorbet

Allow 2 oz (50 g) fresh strawberries per person. Purée, then sweeten with a little sweetener and freeze until mushy. Whip 1 egg white, mix well with the fruit purée, then re-freeze until ready to serve. Garnish with a few strawberries which have had small cuts made in them and been fanned out.

MENU 4

Avocado and prawns with chilli dressing

Coq au vin
Broccoli
Rice and peppers

Lemon syllabub

Avocado and prawns with chilli dressing

Skin and thinly slice 1 avocado pear. Arrange a few slices on each plate. In a small bowl mix a few tablespoons of oil-free french dressing with 1 tablespoon (15 ml) tomato purée. Add a sprinkling of chilli powder and mix well. Allow 1 oz (25 g) shelled prawns per person, dress with the prepared mixture and arrange beside the avocado. Garnish each plate with a twist of lemon. Serve chilled.

Coq au vin

Allow 2 boned and skinned chicken thigh pieces per guest. Marinate the chicken in 10 fl oz (300 ml) good red wine with a bay leaf. In a non-stick pan heat 1 oz (25 g) butter and brown the chicken pieces in it. Slice 2 onions and add to the pan; cook until softened. Sprinkle 1 tablespoon (15 ml) plain flour into the pan and cook, stirring, for 1 minute. Transfer the mixture to a casserole dish. Add the marinade mixture and 10 fl oz (300 ml) hot chicken stock. Add the mushrooms, a sprinkling of thyme, a crushed garlic clove and some ground black pepper. Cook at 180°C/350°F/Gas 4 for 45-50 minutes or until the chicken is cooked. Serve garnished with heart shapes cut from thinly sliced toast.

Broccoli

Allow 3 oz (75 g) per person. Trim, then cook in boiling water until tender. Drain very well.

Rice and peppers

Allow 1 oz (25 g) uncooked rice for yourself and 2-3 oz (50-75 g) each for your guests. Cook as directed on packet. Finely chop some red and green pepper and add to the rice a few minutes before the end of its cooking time.

Lemon syllabub

Finely grate the rind of a large lemon, then pare a few slivers of the peel from another large lemon. Extract the juice from both lemons. Whip 10 fl oz (300 ml) double cream substitute until stiff. Whisk a large egg white until stiff. Add to the cream the grated rind and the lemon juice together with 2 tablespoons (30 ml) dry white wine. Beat the cream again until it holds its shape. Add 1 tablespoon (15 ml) icing sugar. Beat well again. Then fold the whisked egg into the cream mixture. Spoon into individual glasses and chill until set. Decorate each with a few slivers of the pared lemon peel.

Drinks

Remember that if you wish to lose weight you will have to limit your drinking. Allow yourself only a couple of glasses of wine or choose a low-alcohol wine (most of these are so low-calorie that you can have three glasses of one of these to one glass of ordinary wine).

Cheese

You can add a cheese course for your guests and/or serve nibbles and cocktails at the beginning of the meal, but if you partake of either of these yourself you will certainly blow your diet. So if you are weak on willpower don't serve these extras. Likewise, you can treat your friends to mints or chocolates with their coffee, but only if you are strong-willed enough not to indulge yourself. Better to leave these treats until you reach your target weight.

Menus with an international theme

Many enterprising home cooks are adept at preparing whole meals based on a foreign cuisine such as French, Greek or Indian, but a problem may arise for the slimmer because so many of these dishes when cooked authentically contain far too much fat (and therefore calories). However, now that low-fat alternatives are so widely available it is possible to tailor these dishes to your diet and still enjoy them once in a while without blowing your slimming programme entirely. Each recipe contains considerably fewer calories than you would find in their restaurant equivalents, yet they are every bit as good to eat. Each menu is for six people.

FRENCH MENU

Moules marinières

Salmon with spinach
New potatoes

Fruit flambée

Moules marinières

Soak 4 pints (2¼ litres) fresh mussels in cold water, scrub well and pull away the beards. Discard any which are not tightly closed. Put into a large saucepan and pour 10 fl oz (300 ml) dry white wine over the mussels. Chop a large onion and add to the pan with a crushed clove of garlic. If you have some fresh parsley add 1 chopped tablespoon (15 ml) of this. Put a lid on the pan and cook on a gentle heat, shaking gently, for a few minutes until all the mussels have opened. Divide between 6 soup bowls. Pour the cooking liquor over the open mussels.

Salmon with spinach

Allow one salmon steak per guest. Wash 3 lb (1¼ kg) shredded leaf spinach, with the woody stems removed, then cook for a few minutes until reduced. Keep warm while you grill the steaks until the flesh flakes (line the grill first with greased foil to prevent the fish sticking). When the steaks are done, add 2 fl oz (50 ml) double cream substitute to the spinach and mix well. Season with ground black pepper. Arrange a bed of spinach on each guest's plate and top with a salmon steak. Garnish with a wedge of lemon.

New potatoes

Allow 2 oz (50 g) new potatoes for yourself and 4 oz (100 g) for each guest. Cook unpeeled in boiling water until tender.

Fruit flambée

Choose a range of fruits such as banana, apple, peach and orange and cut into attractive shapes. Arrange a selection on each guest's plate. Warm 3 tablespoons (45 ml) brandy, then pour a little over each guest's plate and set alight.

SWISS MENU

Cheese fondue with vegetables

Fresh pineapple in kirsch

Cheese fondue with vegetables

Rub the inside of the fondue pot with a cut clove of garlic, then heat 10 fl oz (300 ml) dry wine wine in it. Grate 1½ lb (600 g) hard low-fat cheese and add to the boiling wine. Stir thoroughly until the cheese has melted. Thicken with 1 teaspoon (5 ml) cornflour mixed with 1 tablespoon (15 ml) kirsch. Place on the table while the mixture is still bubbling. Instead of accompanying with cubes of bread, serve with raw cauliflower, carrot, broccoli, etc.

Fresh pineapple in kirsch

Allow two slices of fresh pineapple per diner. Arrange in a shallow dish and marinate for 2 hours in kirsch. Transfer to individual glass dishes and chill until ready to serve.

ITALIAN MENU

Pasta with creamed cheese sauce

Chicken pizzaiola
Courgettes with lemon
New potatoes

Zabaglione

Pasta with creamed cheese sauce

Allow 1 oz (25 g) raw pasta shells per person. Cook in boiling water until *al dente*. Mix 6 oz (150 g) soft low-fat cheese with 1 crushed clove garlic and a sprinkling of oregano or basil. Purée with a little skimmed milk and 1 tablespoon (15 ml) dry white wine. When the pasta is cooked dress with the sauce and serve immediately.

Chicken pizzaiola

Allow one skinned and boned chicken breast per person. Grill until the chicken is cooked. Meanwhile put 15 oz (375 g) canned chopped tomatoes in a small saucepan with a sprinkling of basil and thyme and a crushed garlic clove. Add 3 tablespoons (45 ml) tomato purée and simmer gently. Quarter 8 oz (200 g) button mushrooms and add with 2 tablespoons (30 ml) white wine to the sauce. Continue cooking until the chicken is cooked, then serve the chicken with the sauce poured over it.

Courgettes with lemon

Take 4 medium courgettes and cut into slices. Heat 1 tablespoon (15 ml) olive oil in a non-stick pan. Quickly stir-fry the courgettes until tender. Add a squeeze of lemon juice and season with ground black pepper.

New potatoes

Allow 2 oz (50 g) potato for yourself and 4 oz (100 g) each for your guests. Cook unpeeled in boiling water until tender.

Zabaglione

Take 6 egg yolks and beat with 3 tablespoons (45 ml) soft brown sugar until the mixture thickens. Place in a heatproof bowl over some boiling water and add 6 tablespoons (90 ml) marsala wine (this is the only suitable wine for this dish) and 1 teaspoon (5 ml) grated lemon rind. Continue beating until the mixture rises slightly and stiffens. Divide between individual dishes and serve immediately.

SPANISH MENU

Gazpacho

Paella

Stuffed figs

Gazpacho

Crumble 1 large slice brown bread, then soak the crumbs in 10 fl oz (300 ml) canned tomato juice. To this mixture add 2 crushed cloves garlic, half a skinned and finely chopped cucumber, 1 red pepper and 1 green pepper, both finely chopped, 1 large chopped onion and 24 oz (600 g) canned chopped tomatoes. Mix well and leave for a few hours. Then liquidize until smooth. Add 2 tablespoons (30 ml) red wine vinegar, 2 tablespoons (30 ml) low-calorie mayonnaise, 2 tablespoons (30 ml) tomato purée. Season with ground black pepper and a sprinkling of oregano. Blend again until smooth. Serve with bowls of diced pepper, onion and cucumber, to which your guests can help themselves.

Paella

In a non-stick pan fry 1 large chopped onion in 1 tablespoon (15 ml) olive oil. Stir in 6 oz (150 g) long-grain rice and 30 fl oz (900 ml) chicken stock. Simmer for 20 minutes or until the rice is tender. Mix in 12 oz (300 g) diced cooked chicken, 6 oz (150 g) shelled prawns, 6 oz (150 g) cooked mussels, 6 oz (150 g) cooked peas, 2 teaspoons (10 ml) paprika. Heat through gently. Serve garnished with unshelled prawns, some cooked mussels (in shell) and lemon wedges.

Stuffed figs

Take 12 dried figs and make a hollow in each. Grate 3 oz (75 g) plain chocolate and mix with 3 oz (75 g) ground almonds, 3 oz (75 g) sultanas and 3 tablespoons (45 ml) orange liqueur. Fill each fig with some of this mixture, then lay, open side upwards, in a shallow baking dish. Bake at 200°C/400°F/Gas 6 for 10 minutes. Then insert a whole almond in each fig before leaving to cool.

AMERICAN MENU

Salad with blue-cheese dressing

Burgers with chilli dressing
Baked jacket potato and sour-cream dressing

Knickerbocker glory

Salad with blue-cheese dressing

Grate together some salad vegetables such as red and white cabbage, carrots and courgettes. Mix with some shredded lettuce, some spinach leaves, watercress and sliced cucumber. Dress with a low-fat blue-cheese dressing.

Burgers with chilli dressing

Split 6 burger buns in half and grill both sides, then grill well 6 4-oz (100-g) beefburgers. Make the chilli dressing by mixing oil-free french dressing with tomato purée and chilli powder. Put the burgers in the buns and top with sliced gherkins, lettuce, sliced onion and chilli dressing.

Jacket potatoes

Bake 3 large potatoes at 220°C/425°F/Gas 7 for 1-1½ hours or until the potatoes are cooked through. Make the dressing by mixing 3 tablespoons (45 ml) sour cream with 3 tablespoons (45 ml) low-calorie mayonnaise and 3 tablespoons (45 ml) chopped chives. Cut each potato into 2 halves and divide the dressing between the potatoes.

Knickerbocker glory

Melt 3 oz (75 g) low-fat plain chocolate in a bowl over some boiling water, then add 3 tablespoons (45 ml) brandy. Pour over vanilla ice cream divided between 6 individual glass dishes. Arrange sliced peaches or nectarines and sliced strawberries alternately on top, and finish each dish with a maraschino cherry.

MEXICAN MENU

Sour-cream dip with corn chips

Tacos

Chocolate and lime pots

Sour-cream dip

Mix 3 tablespoons (45 ml) sour cream with 3 tablespoons (45 ml) low-fat yoghurt and 3 tablespoons (45 ml) low-calorie mayonnaise. Serve with Mexican corn chips (but make sure that you let your guests eat most of these) and crudités.

Tacos

In a non-stick frying-pan heat 1 tablespoon (15 ml) olive oil. Add 1 large chopped onion and fry until soft. Add 18 oz (450 g) lean minced beef and fry until brown. Stir in a crushed clove of garlic and chilli powder to taste. Then add 15 oz (375 g) chopped tomatoes and 3 tablespoons (45 ml) tomato purée. Lower the heat and simmer for 15 minutes until the sauce has thickened. Add 15 oz (375 g) canned red kidney beans and heat through. Pre-heat the oven to 180°C/350°F/Gas 4 and heat 12 taco shells for 2 minutes. Divide the meat mixture between the taco shells and serve with shredded lettuce, sliced tomatoes and 6 oz (150 g) grated low-fat cheese.

Chocolate and lime pots

Melt half a packet of lime jelly in 10 fl oz (300 ml) hot water. Melt 3 oz (75 g) plain chocolate in a bowl over boiling water. Whisk 3 fl oz (45 ml) double cream substitute until soft, then mix all these ingredients together. Divide the mixture between 6 dishes, then chill until set.

CHINESE MENU

Lemon chicken
Chilli prawns
Mushrooms in oyster sauce
Boiled rice

Lychees

Mushrooms in oyster sauce

Thinly slice 12 oz (300 g) mushrooms and stir-fry quickly in 3 tablespoons (45 ml) oyster sauce.

Lemon chicken

Thinly slice 18 oz (450 g) boned, skinned chicken breasts. Extract the juice from 1 lemon. Stir-fry the sliced chicken in 1 tablespoon (15 ml) sesame oil. Add the lemon juice, then thicken with 1 teaspoon (5 ml) cornflour mixed with cold water.

Chilli prawns

Stir-fry 12 oz (300 g) shelled prawns in 1 tablespoon (15 ml) sesame oil. Mix 2 tablespoons (30 ml) tomato purée with chilli powder to taste. Blend to a sauce with 2 tablespoons (30 ml) dry sherry. Add to the prawns and heat through.

Boiled rice

Allow 1 oz (25 g) uncooked rice for yourself and 2-3 oz (50-75 g) each for your guests. Cook as instructed on the packet.

Lychees

Divide two cans of lychees between 6 dishes. Chill well.

MONGOLIAN MENU

Mongolian fire-pot
Salad

Dried fruit salad

Mongolian fire-pot

Remove the skin, bones, giblets and flesh from a 4-lb (1½-kg) chicken. Reserve the flesh, then make a stock by simmering the bones, giblets, a bay leaf, chopped onion and 1¼ pints (750 ml) water for 1 hour. Skim off any scum, then strain. Cut the chicken flesh into bite-sized pieces and arrange on a serving plate. Arrange 12 oz (300 g) shelled prawns on another serving plate. Serve with a salad of diced and sliced vegetables such as mushrooms, peppers, Chinese leaves and water chestnuts. Cook the meat in the stock at the table, using a fondue set. When the meat and prawns have been cooked and eaten, the stock can be divided between the guests as a soup.

Dried fruit salad

Marinate a selection of dried fruits in orange and apple juice overnight. When the fruits have softened divide between 6 dishes and serve with thick low-fat yoghurt.

INDIAN MENU

Chicken tikka masala
Spinach and mushroom bhaji
Boiled rice
Cucumber raita

Mango slices and guava

Chicken tikka masala

Combine 3 tablespoons (45 ml) tandoori curry powder with 1 tablespoon (15 ml) oil, 3 tablespoons (45 ml) lemon juice and 3 tablespoons (45 ml) low-fat natural yoghurt. Cover 4 skinned and boned chicken breasts with this mixture. Leave to marinate overnight. Then cook at 220°C/425°F/Gas 7 for 35 minutes. Chop the chicken into bite-sized pieces. Mix 1 teaspoon (5 ml) Madras curry powder with 5 fl oz (125 ml) water and 5 fl oz (125 ml) single cream substitute, add the rest of the marinade and then simmer gently for 10 minutes. At the end of the cooking time add 1 tablespoon (15 ml) red wine. Serve the chicken with the sauce poured over it.

Spinach and mushroom bhaji

Remove the woody stem from 3 lb (1¼ kg) leaf spinach and shred. Wash thoroughly, then cook until reduced. Add 2 tablespoons (30 ml) oil and 12 oz (300 g) sliced mushrooms. Stir-fry until the mushrooms are cooked. Add 3 tablespoons (45 ml) tomato purée and 2 tablespoons (30 ml) Madras curry powder. Cook until heated through.

Boiled rice

Allow 1 oz (25 g) uncooked rice for yourself and 2-3 oz (50-75 g) each for your guests. Cook as directed on the packet.

Cucumber raita

Thinly slice, then chop, 3 inches (7.5 cm) cucumber, mix with 5 fl oz (125 ml) low-fat natural yoghurt and 1 tablespoon (15 ml) mint sauce. Serve as an accompaniment to the other dishes.

Mango slices and guava

Divide one can of mango slices between 6 dishes. Drain one can of guavas and chop. Divide the guava between the dishes and chill well.

Occasional entertaining

There are certain occasions throughout the year that almost every family celebrates in some way or other, and despite the fact it may be rare for a household to go to town over every event on the calendar there are bound to be times when you want to make a festival memorable. These menus show how to go about it, though of course you can change them round and use them for whatever event you wish. The New Year buffet could be served at any party, especially a cocktail party, while the romantic Valentine's Day dinner need not be confined to 14 February: it would make a superb anniversary dinner for two. Whatever you are celebrating, these menus are bound to provide a few ideas, all within the spirit of your slimming diet.

When entertaining, it is always fun to try to create the right atmosphere as well as providing plenty of good, nourishing food. So use your imagination when setting the table: for example, candles are essential for the Valentine dinner, as are the crackers and mistletoe for the Christmas dinner, while a few small, low-level bowls of flowers would set the mood for the Midsummer Eve celebration.

Lastly, don't forget that even though you may have done all the work, or the lion's share of it, *you* are supposed to be enjoying yourself too. It is always hard for guests to relax and have a good time when their host or hostess is forever flapping around. Relax, try to ensure that you do as much as possible beforehand and make sure that if you know you will need a hand someone will be ready to help you.

NEW YEAR BUFFET PARTY (FOR 30)

Your guests will probably be much more interested in drinking than eating, but it is always advisable to have some interesting canapés on hand that people can nibble at as well as a few more substantial sandwiches, to absorb the alcohol. If you also put out some crisps and nuts make sure that you keep well away from them – they are fatal for slimmers, and it is impossible to keep track of how much of them you have eaten. For yourself, decide ahead of the party that you will have only one of each canapé – and then stick to your New Year's resolution!

Prawn and sesame triangles
Nutty chicken pieces
Caviar toasts
Salmon and melon on sticks
Ham and turkey sticks
Dips and crudités
Assorted sandwiches

Prawn and sesame triangles

Roll out a bought 8-oz (200-g) packet of shortcrust pasty to a 16 × 8 inch (40 × 20 cm) oblong. Finely chop 16 oz (400 g) shelled prawns, then add a sprinkling of chilli powder, a crushed clove of garlic and 2 tablespoons (30 ml) tomato purée. Mix well, then beat an egg and use to brush the pastry. Add the remaining beaten egg to the prawn mixture. Now spread this mixture over the pastry and sprinkle with sesame seeds. Cut into 32 squares, then cut each square diagonally to make triangles. Place on greased baking trays and cook at 200°C/400°F/Gas 6 for 10-15 minutes or until golden brown. Serve cold.

Nutty chicken pieces

Cut 16 oz (400 g) skinned and boned chicken up into bite-sized pieces and marinate this in a mixture of 4 tablespoons (60 ml) crunchy peanut butter, 2 tablespoons (30 ml) dark brown sugar and 2 tablespoons (30 ml) each of soy sauce and lemon juice. Stir thoroughly every 30 minutes for 2 hours. Place, leaving gaps between each piece, on greased baking trays, and cook at 200° C/400°F/Gas 6 for 10 minutes or until the chicken is cooked through. Spike with cocktail sticks or make into mini-kebabs by skewering with small pieces of banana and cucumber.

Caviar toasts

Make plenty of wholemeal toast, then spread with soft low-fat cheese. On top of this spread patterns of red and black cod's roe. Then cut the bread up into small squares.

Salmon and melon on sticks

Cut 8 oz (200 g) smoked salmon into 30 strips. De-seed and peel some melon and cut strips about 1 ×2 inches (2.5 × 5 cm). Wrap each salmon strip round a piece of melon and secure with a cocktail stick.

Ham and turkey sticks

Cut 4 oz (100 g) lean ham into thin strips. Cut some cooked turkey into bite-sized pieces, then wrap a piece of ham round each one and secure with a cocktail stick.

Dips and crudités

Make two different dips by mixing two different types of low-fat dressing with low-fat yoghurt. Surround each dip with strips of raw vegetable such as carrot, pepper, celery or cucumber and some oddments on sticks, such as cauliflower and button mushrooms.

Assorted sandwiches

Using a mixture of wholemeal and high-fibre white bread make up assorted sandwiches using a low-fat spread and fillings such as low-fat pâté, sardine and tomato paste, dressed crab, tuna (canned in brine and drained) mixed with low-calorie mayonnaise, lean turkey or ham. Pad each sandwich out with some salad vegetables.

VALENTINE DINNER (FOR 2)

Spiced prawns with heart-shaped toasts

Fillet steak with passion-fruit sauce
Green salad
Marinated mushrooms

Apricot and brandy fool

Spiced prawns with heart-shaped toasts

Melt 1 oz (25 g) butter, then mix with 3 oz (75 g) shelled prawns and 1 teaspoon (5 ml) paprika. Add a little ground black pepper and a squeeze of lemon juice. Mix well and divide the mixture between two ramekin dishes; press the mixture into each dish. Top each dish with a little more melted butter, then chill until the butter has set. Make 2 slices of toast, cut 1 heart shape out of each and serve with the prawns.

Fillet steak with passion-fruit sauce

Grill 2 fillet steaks well: yours should be 4 oz (100 g) uncooked weight. To make the sauce, melt a little redcurrant jelly and add 2 tablespoons (30 ml) sherry and the pulp from 2 passion fruit. Pour over the steaks.

Green salad

Mix together shredded lettuce leaves and watercress and serve with an oil-free french dressing.

Marinated mushrooms

In a non-stick pan fry 8 oz (200 g) button mushrooms. Add a sprinkling of thyme and 4 fl oz (120 ml) red wine. Bring to the boil, then simmer for 2-3 minutes. Transfer to a glass dish, season with ground black pepper, toss well and leave to marinate for at least 2 hours. Bring to room temperature before serving.

Apricot and brandy fool

Simmer 1 oz (25 g) fresh apricots with 5 fl oz (125 ml) water for 20-30 minutes or until tender. Leave to cool. Purée 5 oz (125 g) canned apricots in natural juice with their liquid, then add to the cooled apricots. Mix well. Add 2 tablespoons (30 ml) brandy. Whisk 2 tablespoons (30 ml) double cream substitute until stiff and fold into the fruit purée. Chill until ready to eat.

EASTER LUNCH (FOR 6)

Scallop salad

Lamb with fresh vegetables

Drunken fruit jelly

Scallop salad

You will need 12 scallops (but only 6 scallop shells). Slice the white of each scallop thinly, reserving the coral. Marinate the sliced scallops in lime juice for 2 hours. Then drain and arrange the slices in each scallop shell. Top each with 1 tablespoon (15 ml) black cod's roe and the reserved coral. Chill until ready to serve.

Lamb with fresh vegetables

You will need 2 racks of lamb (each with 6 cutlets). If the meat is not trimmed, remove all the fat. Spread a mixture made from 2 teaspoons (10 ml) clear honey and 2 teaspoons (10 ml) Dijon mustard over one side of the lamb. Roast at 200 °C/400°F/Gas 6 for 35-40 minutes (the lamb should be slightly pink). Carve the racks so that each guest gets 2 cutlets.

Cut a selection of dwarf corn, baby carrots and mange-tout and decorate each guest's plate with these.

New potatoes may also be served, to your guests.

Drunken fruit jelly

Make some melon balls from an ogen melon, mix with 2 peeled and sliced kiwi fruit and 8 oz (200 g) halved and seeded black grapes. Make up a lime jelly substituting 5 fl oz (125 ml) dry white wine and 2 fl oz (50 ml) port for some of the water. Divide the fruits between 6 glasses, then pour the jelly over, mix well and leave to set.

MIDSUMMER EVE SUPPER (FOR 6)

At this time of abandonment and frivolity, I always tend to go for dishes with a pink or green colour theme. The meal should be a long, leisurely affair – ideally, if the weather permits, eaten in the garden. Choose rosé or sparkling white wines to accompany it. Bubbles always tend to go to people's heads, which makes for an evening of midsummer madness!

Artichokes with lemon dressing

Salmon steaks
Pink and green salad
New potatoes

Summer pudding

Artichokes with lemon dressing

Allow 1 artichoke per person. Trim the leaves and the base so that each will stand upright, Boil for 30-40 minutes until a leaf will pull out easily. Leave to cool. Mix 6 tablespoons (90 ml) oil-free french dressing with 6 tablespoons (90 ml) lemon juice, add some ground black pepper and mix well. Serve each artichoke surrounded by lemon dressing.

Salmon steaks

Poach the salmon steaks in a mixture of dry white wine and water for a few minutes or until the flesh flakes easily. Dress with a little lemon juice and ground black pepper and leave to cool.

Pink and green salad

Make a salad from a head of radicchio and some curly endive, peel and thinly slice an avocado and add to the salad. Add some red geranium petals (if available) or scented geranium leaves. Serve with a light dressing made 1 tablespoon (15 ml) each of olive oil, lemon juice and orange juice.

New potatoes

Allow yourself 2 oz (50 g) potato and 4 oz (100 g) each for your guests. Cook unpeeled in boiling water until tender. Leave to cool.

Summer pudding

Use 5 slices of crustless wholemeal bread to line a 1-pint (900-ml) pudding basin. From another slice cut a circle large enough to cover the top of the basin. Mix 8 oz (200 g) strawberries with 4 oz (100 g) raspberries and 4 oz (100 g) mixed redcurrants and black-currants. Stew the fruit with 2 tablespoons (30 ml) red wine for about 5 minutes until it starts to soften. Fill the basin with the fruit and soak the bread with the juices. Top with the remaining circle of bread, put a saucer on top and weigh it down with a can (or something of similar weight). Leave in a cool place overnight. Turn out on to a serving dish and serve with creamy Greek yoghurt.

SUMMER BARBECUE (FOR 8)

Fish steaks
Spicy chicken kebabs
Green salad
Tomato salad
New potatoes

Strawberry, kiwi and lychee salad

Fish steaks

Brush either mackerel, cod or haddock fillets with a little oil and season with tarragon or thyme and some ground black pepper. On a hot barbecue, they should need only a few minutes' cooking per side.

Spicy chicken kebabs

Marinate 4 boned and skinned chicken breasts, cut into 2-inch (5-cm) chunks, in a mixture of red wine, chilli powder and soy sauce. Thread on to skewers, alternating with blanched button mushrooms, quartered onions and banana chunks. Cook on a barbecue, turning regularly until the chicken is cooked through.

Green salad

Shred some lettuce leaves and mix with watercress, sliced kiwi fruit and sliced celery. Garnish with some poppy seeds. Serve an oil-free dressing as accompaniment.

Tomato salad

Shred a few Chinese leaves and mix with 8 sliced tomatoes and some chopped red pepper. Add a handful of stoned black olives. Dress with some mixed herbs and lemon juice.

New potatoes

Allow 2 oz (50 g) potatoes for yourself and 4 oz (100 g) each for your guests. Cook unpeeled in boiling water until tender. Serve cold.

Strawberry, kiwi and lychee salad

Hull and halve 8 oz (200 g) strawberries, peel and slice 2 kiwi fruit and mix the two fruits with the drained contents of 2 cans of lychees. Marinate in 2 tablespoons (30 ml) red wine. Serve chilled.

SUNDAY BRUNCH (FOR 8)

These are becoming ever more popular, particularly amongst childless couples, who generally manage to get a lie-in on Sunday mornings. For such people brunch, a combination of breakfast and lunch, is ideal. It is usual to serve fresh orange juice for those who find late morning too early in the day to drink and a wine cup for those who think it is never too early to drink! And don't forget to serve non-alcoholic wine (which is what you should be drinking).

Cold chicken
Waldorf salad
Kedgeree
Ham, bacon and mushroom kebabs
Grapefruit and melon cocktail

Cold chicken

Roast a 3-lb (1¼-kg) chicken, then leave to cool. When cool, carve into thin slices and arrange on a serving plate. Garnish with mandarin oranges.

Waldorf salad

Core and slice thinly 2 green apples and 1 red apple. Thinly slice 4 sticks celery, then mix with 2 oz (50 g) shelled walnuts and shredded lettuce. Dress all the ingredients with a mixture made from 4 tablespoons (60 ml) low-calorie mayonnaise and 4 tablespoons (60 ml) low-fat natural yoghurt. Season with ground back pepper.

Kedgeree

Cook 1 lb (400 g) brown long-grain rice. Poach 1 large haddock, remove the flesh and flake. In a non-stick pan cook 2 chopped onions in 1 tablespoon (15 ml) oil until golden. Hard-boil 2 eggs and reserve one of the yolks. Chop the rest of the eggs up. Mix everything except the reserved yolk with some ground black pepper and a sprinkling of curry powder. Pile into a serving bowl, chop the remaining yolk and sprinkle over the top.

Ham, bacon and mushroom kebabs

Cube some lean ham and slice some streaky bacon. Roll each little strip of bacon up. Thread alternately with some small button mushrooms on wooden skewers. Grill until the bacon is well cooked.

Grapefruit and melon cocktail

Mix grapefruit segments with fresh melon balls and serve cold.

HALLOWEEN DINNER (FOR 8)

Pumpkin soup

Stuffed chicken and cranberry sauce
Rice pilaff

Rich walnut cake

Pumpkin soup

This is a sensational soup for starting the evening off. Cut the top off a large whole pumpkin, one which will yield about 3 lb (1¼ kg) flesh, about a quarter of the way down. Scoop out the inside, leaving a shell about 1 inch (2.5 cm) thick. Rub the inside with a little oil. Dice the flesh, then set aside. Heat 2 tablespoons (30 ml) oil in a large saucepan and fry 2 teaspoons (10 ml) ground ginger and 1 teaspoon (5 ml) ground coriander in it. Now add 1 large chopped onion, 2 chopped carrots and the pumpkin flesh to the pan. Simmer on a low heat for 20 minutes until the pumpkin is mushy. Add 1½ pints (900 ml) chicken stock and simmer gently for another 20 minutes. Add a squeeze of lemon juice and some ground black pepper and liquidize until smooth. Add a little skimmed milk if the soup is too thick. Pour the soup into the hollowed-out shell, which now becomes a tureen.

Stuffed chicken with cranberry sauce

Allow 1 boned, skinned chicken breast per person. Make up 4 oz (100 g) packet stuffing and add a squeeze of lemon, 4 oz (100 g) chopped mushrooms and 2 teaspoons (10 ml) french mustard. Use this to stuff each breast cavity, rolling the chicken fillet well round the stuffing and securing with a cocktail stick. Wrap each individually in foil and cook in a pre-heated oven at 200°C/400° F/Gas 6 for 50-60 minutes until cooked.

For the sauce, heat 3 tablespoons (45 ml) cranberry jelly with tablespoons (45 ml) orange juice and 2 tablespoons (30 ml) port. Mix well and serve hot.

Rice pilaff

Cook 12 oz (300 g) brown long-grain rice; mix with 2 oz (50 g) grilled pine nuts and 2 oz (50 g) stoned black olives. Throw in a handful of chopped fresh parsley if available.

Rich walnut cake

This is rather tiring to make unless you have a food processor but is well worth the trouble.

Whisk 3 large egg yolks with 3 oz (75 g) soft light brown sugar. Whisk or 15 minutes by hand (or 5 minutes in a food processor) until pale and frothy. Pre-heat the oven to 180°C/350°F/Gas 4. Grease a non-stick ring tin. Melt 1 oz (25 g) butter and add with 4 oz (100 g) ground walnuts and 1 tablespoon (15 ml) cold strong coffee to the egg yolks. Whisk the egg whites until stiff, then fold into the yolk mixture. Pour into the tin and bake for 35 minutes or until a skewer comes out clean. Turn out to cool on a wire rack. Dust with a little icing sugar before serving.

GUY FAWKES PARTY (FOR 8)

Mulled wine

Jacket potatoes
Barbecued beans
Grilled sausages
Cream cheese coleslaw

Christmas pudding

Mulled wine

Heat 10 fl oz (250 ml) orange juice, 2 bottles red wine, 1 tablespoon (15 ml) honey, 4 cloves and a 2-inch (5-cm) stick of cinnamon for 10 minutes. Strain, then serve hot.

Jacket potatoes

Cook 8 small jacket potatoes at 220°C/425°F/Gas 7 for 60 minutes or until cooked through. Make a cross in each one and top with a little low-fat spread.

Barbecued beans

Heat 2 cans barbecued beans with 2 tablespoons (30 ml) tomato purée and 1 tablespoon (15 ml) soy sauce. Serve hot.

Grilled sausages

Grill 8 low-fat sausages well, turning frequently until cooked through.

Cream cheese coleslaw

Shred half a medium white cabbage. Add to 3 chopped celery sticks and 2 finely grated medium carrots. Purée 4 oz (100 g) soft low-fat cheese spread with 2 tablespoons (30 ml) skimmed milk and a half-and-half mix of low-fat natural yoghurt and low-calorie mayonnaise. Dress the coleslaw with this mixture.

Christmas pudding

This always seems to go down well at Guy Fawkes parties, maybe because it comes as such a surprise to guests.

Cook 1 small Christmas pudding as directed on the packaging. Serve with a little single cream substitute mixed with a little brandy.

SPECIAL CHRISTMAS DINNER (FOR 4)

If you are a childless couple and don't want to spend Christmas with the family, why not get together with another couple and have a special Christmas dinner that is a little out of the ordinary?

Crab and prawn cocktail

Stuffed turkey breasts
Stir-fried broccoli and carrots
Swede and potato duchesse

Christmas pudding creams

Crab and prawn cocktail

Mix 4 oz (100 g) white crab meat with 4 oz (100 g) shelled prawns. Stir in 4 tablespoons (60 ml) low-calorie Thousand Island dressing. Season with ground black pepper and serve on a bed of shredded lettuce in tall glasses, garnished with lemon twists.

Stuffed turkey breasts

Stuff the cavities of 2 large turkey breasts with a mixture made from 2 oz (50 g) packet stuffing, some chopped apricot, 4 oz (100 g) chopped mushroom and a sprinkling of almond flakes. Make sure the fillet is well wrapped round the stuffing. Roast at 180°C/350°F/Gas 4 for 60-70 minutes or until the turkey is cooked through. Leave to stand for 10 minutes before carving, then re-heat the meat before serving.

For the sauce, heat 2 tablespoons (30 ml) cranberry sauce with 2 tablespoons (30 ml) port and the pulp from 2 passion fruit.

Stir-fried broccoli and carrots

Cook 12 oz (300 g) carrots, cut into matchsticks, in boiling water for 4 minutes. Add 8 oz (200 g) broccoli florets and cook for another minute. Drain. Heat 1 tablespoon (15 ml) oil in a non-stick pan, add 1 teaspoon (5 ml) ground ginger and then the vegetables. Stir-fry for 3 minutes or until the vegetables are cooked.

Swede and potato duchesse

Boil 1 lb (400 g) potato and 8 oz (200 g) swede until cooked. Mash with 2 tablespoons (30 ml) skimmed milk, 3 oz (75 g) soft low-fat cheese and 1 oz (25 g) low-fat spread. Season with ground black pepper. Then pipe in large rosettes on to a greased baking tray. Bake at 180°C/350°F/Gas 4 for 30 minutes.

Christmas pudding creams

Marinate for 1 hour 2 oz (50 g) chopped glacé cherries, 2 oz (50 g) raisins and 2 oz (50 g) sultanas and 4 tablespoons (60 ml) rum. Beat 2 egg yolks with 1 oz (25 g) soft light brown sugar until pale and frothy. Melt 2 oz (50 g) plain chocolate and add to 4 fl oz (120 ml) single cream substitute. Add these to the yolk mixture and heat in a glass bowl over boiling water until the mixture starts to thicken. Whisk 4 fl oz (120 ml) double cream substitute and fold the egg mixture into this. Freeze until mushy. Stir well and add the fruit, rum marinade and 2 oz (50 g) flaked almonds. Divide the mixture between 4 ramekin dishes and freeze until firm.

6 Judgement Day

At last comes that wonderful day when the scales finally register the weight you have been aiming to be. It's not always the wonderful day that you had hoped for: you may find that you still need to lose a few pounds. On the other hand you may find that you look too skinny (a thought that seems unbelievable when you have weight to lose): if people start to tell you that you look ill, believe them and gain a few pounds. This is the stage where some people are in danger of becoming anorexic, for it is easy to believe that you still need to lose a few pounds when in fact you look wonderful. Don't take any chances with your health: always play safe, and if you are worried, consult your doctor.

Now that you have reached your desired weight, don't think that that is the end of it – because it certainly isn't. If you drop all of the good eating habits that you have got into you will soon see those pounds slipping back on again, wasting months of effort. Although you can ease up on watching your weight you certainly cannot forget about it entirely. To get to the weight that you are now at, you have been consuming fewer calories than your body needs to run efficiently.

Therefore you can now increase your food intake *slightly* so that you don't continue to lose weight.

The best way to do this is to increase marginally the amount of carbohydrate – potato, pasta, rice or bread – that you have been eating as your main meal. You can also slightly increase the amount of the protein food you eat at your main meal, e.g. the chicken, fish, dairy foods, egg or pulses that you eat. You could also widen the range of meats you eat, to include fattier types, but you should still eat red meats only occasionally.

Whilst you have been engaged in sinful slimming you have been eating a healthy diet. If you now continue to follow this way of eating you will not go far wrong. I would suggest that you become a regular subscriber to one of the slimming magazines, too. If you read these on a regular basis, you will become far better informed about food and what is and isn't good for you. They are also full of interesting recipes which will make sure that you never run out of ideas for healthy dishes that taste delicious and will not put those lost pounds back on.

While following your diet you have probably become much more aware of all the many items for which low-fat equivalents now exist. The range of low-fat foods will doubtless continue to increase now that manufacturers have discovered that shoppers are concerned about what they and their families eat and are unwilling to risk eating too many high-fat foods.

Of course, now that you have reached your target weight you can also allow yourself more of the items that until recently you have had to assess in terms of Cheat Units. But it is important to remember that these are *not* the building blocks of a good, healthy diet: they are items that you should still regard as special treats and such foods are worth more if they are not indulged in too often.

There will inevitably be times, maybe on your holiday or during the Christmas period, when you put on a few pounds. Tackle these quickly. If you leave them a while, a few more will probably join them. Revert to the diet for a week or so and you should be back to normal.

Perhaps now that you are in better shape you will not be so exercise-resistant. You may indeed find that your new shape gives you more energy, and that you are happier to go swimming or play football with the kids, or have a girls'/boys' night out playing badminton. Perhaps you can last longer on the dance floor with your partner now. Do take advantage of the extra energy that you now have. It is true that the more that you put into life the more you get out of it. But don't forget to take time out for yourself: a long, relaxing bath after a hard day can do wonders, and a long, lazy walk by yourself in attractive surroundings can remind you of what life is all about.

All in all, you should start to enjoy your life more, because what you have done is gain a little more control over it. Make sure that you *stay* in control and you will find that you have a more relaxed view of life.

Here are some tips to ensure that you stay on the right path.

Stay-slim tips

(1) Make sure that you continue to cut as much fat as possible out of your diet.
(2) Try to keep to three meals a day. It is dangerous to get into the habit of eating snacks whenever you feel peckish.
(3) Cut out as much sugar as you can. It is no use to you.
(4) Whenever you have the choice, go for high-fibre foods, such as wholemeal bread, wholemeal pasta and brown rice. Fibre is good for you as it fills you up and does wonders for your digestion.
(5) Make sure that you keep your intake of alcohol down. Like sugar it is full of empty calories.
(6) Always use the low-fat, sugar-free or low-calorie alternatives to manufactured foods such as yoghurt, mayonnaise, cream, soup, baked beans, cheese, canned fruit and so on, if there is one.
(7) Try to include some form of exercise in your daily routine: it will do wonders for your shape.
(8) If you are weak-willed don't keep foods in the house that

will encourage you to nibble – remember, you're a born sinner!

(9) Promise yourself that you won't let yourself get overweight again. Keep looking at yourself in the mirror and appreciate your new shape. Don't forget you really did this for yourself – and it would be you who would suffer if you let that weight go back on again.

My last tip is for the many women who find that they put on weight when they become pregnant which they find hard to lose when the baby is born. Having a baby is *not* an excuse to lose your shape permanently. There is no reason to put on excess weight. Follow your doctor's advice and you won't go far wrong, and do follow the principles of healthy eating and regular exercise on which the 'sinful slimming' system is based.

The maintenance diets that follow are only guides. If you get used to these it won't be long before you are devising your own weekly menus.

Spring menus

Grilled chicken served with broccoli, courgettes and new potatoes

Roast or casseroled lamb served with cabbage, carrots and mashed potatoes

Portion of pizza served with a green salad and a potato salad made with an oil-free dressing

Smoked mackerel served with a mixed salad and new potatoes

Grilled trout served with broad beans and new potatoes

Tuna and sweetcorn heated with low-fat dressing and served with tagliatelle and green salad

Grilled lamb cutlets served with cabbage, carrots and new potatoes

Summer menus

Grilled chicken served with mushrooms, broccoli and new potatoes

Grilled lamb served with broad beans, cauliflower and new potatoes

Bean salad made with red kidney beans, butter beans, sweetcorn, herbs and oil-free french dressing, served with pasta and a green salad

Tuna salad on wholemeal bread, served with coleslaw made with an oil-free dressing and a green salad

Smoked mackerel served with a green salad and new potatoes

Prawn and cod casserole cooked in a mixture of white wine and cream substitute, served with rice pilaff

Crab or lobster served with a mixed salad and new potatoes or rice

Autumn menus

Grilled pork chops served with new potatoes, puréed spinach and carrots

Grilled chicken served with peas, carrots and jacket potato

Small portion of quiche served with green salad and coleslaw made with an oil-free dressing

Beef stew made with red wine and tomatoes and served with brussels sprouts, carrots and creamed potatoes

Grilled gammon steaks served with barbecued beans, grilled tomatoes and new potatoes

Grilled mackerel served with puréed swede, peas and new potatoes

Stuffed cabbage, courgette or marrow served with thick tomato sauce, peas and creamed potatoes

Winter menus

Roasted or casseroled beef served with cabbage, mashed turnips, roast parsnips and potatoes

Grilled pork chop served with brussels sprouts, swede and boiled potatoes

Chopped bacon and mushrooms cooked in a low-fat spread and egg mixture, served with tagliatelle and green salad

Lentil curry served with curried spinach, mushrooms and rice

Tuna and ratatouille served with pasta shells

Cod, casseroled or grilled, served with peas, carrots and creamed potato

Grilled chicken served with leeks, peas and jacket potato

Index of Recipes

Calorie Guide

	cals. per 25 g/ 1 oz, 2.5 ml/ 1 fl oz	cals. per 100 g/4 oz or as stated
Almonds, shelled	170	
Anchovies, canned	50	
Apples, fresh	12	50
juice	10	50 (150 ml/¼ pint)
sauce, sweetened	30	
stewed without sugar	9	36
crumble	63	252
pie, double crust, short pastry	73	292
turnover		400 (1 medium)
Apricots, raw	8	30 (2-3)
stewed, fresh, without sugar	6	25
canned in syrup	30	120
dried, uncooked	74	
dried, stewed without sugar	17	70
Artichokes		
globe, boiled	4	24 (1 medium)
Jerusalem, boiled	5	20
Asparagus, boiled whole spears	5	20 (apx. 6 spears)
Aubergine, boiled	4	
Avocado	25	125 (½ medium)

	cals. per 25 g/ 1 oz, 2.5 ml/ 1 fl oz	cals. per 100 g/4 oz or as stated
Biscuits		
chocolate		80-140 each
digestive	135	60 each
ginger	128	33 each
sweet	128	40-70 each
Blackberries, raw	15	
stewed without sugar	10	40
canned in syrup	30	120
Blackcurrants, raw	7	
stewed, without sugar	6	25
canned in syrup	30	120
Bovril	35	5 (per cup made from 1 teaspoon)
Brandy (standard pub measure		75
Brazil nuts, shelled	183	
Bread (average slice 25 g/l oz)		
brown	68	
malt	71	
slimmers' low-calorie breads		37 (average per slice)
white	70	
wholemeal	63	

	cals. per 25 g/ 1 oz, 2.5 ml/ 1 fl oz	cals. per 100 g/4 oz or as stated
Caerphilly	98	
Camembert	85	
cottage	30	
with pineapple		91
Cheddar	120	
Cheshire	110	
cream	230	
curd	40	
Danish blue	100	
Edam	85	
Emmenthal	113	
Gloucester	114	
Gorgonzola	110	
Gouda	95	
Gruyère	130	
Lancashire	100	
mozzarella	96	
parmesan	120	
processed	105	
smoked	76	
Stilton	135	
Wensleydale	115	
Cheesecake		306 (apx.)
Cheese soufflé		247 (apx.)

Bacon (rashers)		
grilled back	114	170 (apx. 2 rashers)
grilled gammon	94	140 (apx. 1 rasher)
grilled streaky	145	185 (apx. 2 rashers)
Bananas	22	65 (1 medium)
Beans		
baked, in tomato sauce	26	104
broad, boiled	12	48
butter, boiled	26	105
french, boiled	8	32
haricot, boiled	25	100
runner, boiled	2	10
canned, kidney	26	104
Beef		
corned, canned	65	260
minced, raw	76	(depending on fat content)
roast topside, lean only	70	280
roast sirloin, lean only	65	260
steak, grilled, lean	85	340
steak, stewed, lean	60	240
steak and kidney pie with flaky pastry	86	516 (175 g/6 oz)
stew with vegetables	40	240 (175 g/6 oz)
stock cube		15 (1 cube)
Beer		
bitter, draught		75 (300 ml/½ pint)
lager		75 (300 ml/½ pint)
shandy		100 (300 ml/½ pint)
Beetroot, pickled	8	

stuffing mix	104	
sauce	30	
Broccoli, boiled	4	15
Brown sauce, bottled		20 (1 tablespoon)
Brussels sprouts, boiled	5	20
Butter	225	
Cabbage, raw	5	
boiled	2	10
Cakes		(all apx.)
chocolate		285 (50-g/2-oz slice)
coffee		283 (50-g/2-oz slice)
Dundee		222 (50-g/2-oz slice)
gingerbread		218 (50-g/2-oz slice)
plain fruit		216 (50-g/2-oz slice)
swiss roll with jam		180 (50-g/2-oz slice)
sponge		176 (50-g/2-oz slice)
Campari (standard pub measure)		120
Carrots, raw	8	
boiled	6	25
Cashew nuts	159	
roasted and salted	177	
Cauliflower, raw	8	
boiled	3	10
Caviar	74	
Celery, raw	2	10 (apx. 2 sticks)
boiled	1	4
Cheese		
Brie	95	

Cheese straws	172	
Cherries, raw	12	
glacé	96	
canned in syrup	25	100
Chestnuts, shelled	50	
Chicken, roast	54	215
liver	44	
pie		396 (175 g/6 oz) (apx.)
stock cube		8 (each)
Chicory	3	
Chilli sauce		17 (1 tablespoon)
Chives	8	
Chocolate		
drinking (1 cup made with milk, no sugar)	115	175
éclair		150 (medium)
milk	165	335 (small bar)
plain	155	310 (small bar)
Christmas pudding		350 (apx.)
Chutney		
apple	57	
mango	52	
Cider		
dry	10	100 (300 ml/½ pint)
sweet	12	120 (300 ml/½ pint)
Coca-Cola	12	120 (300 ml/½ pint)
Cocoa		
1 cup made with milk, no sugar		160

	cals. per 25 g/ 1 oz, 2.5 ml/ 1 fl oz	cals. per 100 g/4 oz or as stated
Coconut, fresh	98	
desiccated	175	
Cod, raw, flesh only	22	
steamed		90
Coffee		
1 cup, black, no sugar		0
1 cup with 25 ml/1 fl oz milk and 2 teaspoons sugar		95
Coleslaw		
with french dressing	27	
with mayonnaise	41	
Cornflour	100	
Corn oil	260	
Courgettes, raw	5	
boiled	3	12
Crab, boiled	35	
Crackers		
cream	110	38 (each)
Cranberries	4	
sauce	48	
Cream		
double	130	650 (150 ml/5 oz)
single	62	310 (150 ml/5 oz)
soured	60	300 (150 ml/5 oz)

	cals. per 25 g/ 1 oz, 2.5 ml/ 1 fl oz	cals. per 100 g/4 oz or as stated
Fruit gums	68	
Fruit and nut chocolate	140	
Fruit fool (depending on fruit)		80 (apx.)
Fruit salad, canned in syrup	27	108
Fruit tart		240 (apx.)
Garlic	39	
Gelatine	70	
Gin (standard pub measure)		55
Ginger ale		88 (225-ml/8½-oz bottle)
American dry		36 (225-ml/8½-oz bottle)
Ginger, ground	74	
root	13	
Gooseberries, raw	10	
stewed without sugar	5	20
canned in syrup	22	88
Grapefruit		
raw		15 (½ medium)
juice, unsweetened	11	55 (150 ml/¼ pint)
squash, undiluted	35	

	cals. per 25 g/ 1 oz, 2.5 ml/ 1 fl oz	cals. per 100 g/4 oz or as stated
Kippers, baked or grilled	57	228
Lamb		
grilled chop		435
roast leg	82	330
roast shoulder	96	385
Lasagne	30	180 (175 g/6 oz)
Leeks, boiled	7	30
Lemon		15 (1)
juice, unsweetened	2	10 (150 ml/¼ pint)
squash, undiluted	35	
barley water	26	
Lemonade	7	70 (300 ml/½ pint)
Lentils, dry	96	
boiled	27	
Lettuce	3	
Lime juice cordial, undiluted	30	
Liqueurs		
Benedictine	112	
Brandy	65	
Cherry brandy	100	
Crème de menthe	112	
Drambuie	110	
Kirsch	83	

Food		
Crispbread		17-21 (depending on brand)
Crumpets	54	
Currants	70	
Curry powder	70	
Custard made with powder, milk and sugar	30	
Damsons, stewed without sugar	8	
Dates	60	
Doughnut		235 (1)
Dried mixed fruit	86	
Dubonnet (per wine glass)		170
Duck, roast	88	355
Eggs		
raw, poached, boiled		90 (1)
fried		135 (1)
scotch	50	200
scrambled (with milk and butter)		200 (1)
Fish cakes, made with potato and egg	49	98 (50 g/2 oz)
Fish fingers	50	190 (4)
Fish paste	50	25 (12 g/½ oz)
Flour, plain white	103	
self-raising	96	
wholemeal	94	
canned segments	19	76
Grapes	17	70
juice	14	70 (150 ml/¼ pint)
Haddock, fried		220
smoked	29	117
steamed or grilled	28	112
Ham, boiled lean	62	250
Hamburger		160 (each) (apx.)
Hazelnuts, shelled	180	
Herbs, mixed dried		9 (1 teaspoon)
Herring, fresh	50	
fried in oatmeal	67	268
baked	54	216
soused or pickled	63	252
Honey	80	40 (12 g/½ oz)
Horseradish		
creamed	57	
sauce	25	
Ice cream, vanilla	55	110 (50 g/2 oz)
Jam, fruit with seeds or stone fruit	74	37 (12 g/½ oz)
Jam roll, baked	115	345 (75 g/3 oz)
Jam tart	112	448
Jelly, made up	17	70
Kidney, lamb, grilled	28	112
ox, braised	71	284
Tia Maria	92	
Liver		
calf's raw or grilled	40	160
fried with flour	74	296
chicken, raw or grilled	44	176
lamb's, raw or grilled	38	152
pâté	78	
sausage	90	
Lobster, boiled, flesh	26	105
Loganberries, fresh	5	
stewed without sugar	4	16
canned in syrup	29	116
Lucozade	21	105 (150 ml/¼ pint)
Luncheon meat, pork canned	95	380
Macaroni, dry	105	
boiled	42	168
cheese	60	240
Mackerel, grilled	54	216
smoked	62	248
Mandarin oranges, canned	17	
Margarine	225	
slimmers'	105	
Marmalade	75	
Marrow, boiled	2	10
Marzipan	116	
Mayonnaise	200	100 (1 tablespoon)
Melon, honeydew		24 (medium slice)
Meringues	112	

	cals. per 25 g/ 1 oz, 2.5 ml/ 1 fl oz	cals. per 100 g/4 oz or as stated
Milk, fresh whole	19	190 (300 ml/½ pint)
fresh, skimmed	10	100 (300 ml/½ pint)
dried, low-fat skimmed (powder)	90	90 (300 ml/½ pint)
condensed sweetened	100	
evaporated	45	225 (150 ml/¼ pint)
Mincemeat	77	
pie		373
Minestrone soup		100 (300 ml/½ pint)
Mint sauce	44	
Mixed peel	68	
Muesli	105	
Mullet, red or grey, stewed	36	144
Mushrooms, raw	2	
fried	62	125 (50 g/2 oz)
canned cream soup	15	150 (300 ml/½ pint)
Mussels, boiled	25	100
Mustard (English)	132	5 (1 teaspoon made up)
Mustard and cress	3	
Nectarines	14	25 (1)
Noodles, dry	110	
boiled	35	
Nutmeg		20 (1 teaspoon)

	cals. per 25 g/ 1 oz, 2.5 ml/ 1 fl oz	cals. per 100 g/4 oz or as stated
Peanuts		
butter	180	93 (1 tablespoon)
shelled	170	
roasted and salted	182	
Pears, fresh	10	40 (1 medium)
stewed without sugar	8	32
canned in syrup	22	88
Peas, fresh boiled	14	55
dried boiled	28	110
dried, split, boiled	33	132
canned	24	96
soup	11	110 (300 ml/½ pint)
Peppers, raw		40 (1 medium)
Pickle, sweet	37	
Pineapple, fresh	13	25 (1 medium slice)
juice	14	70 (150 ml/¼ pint)
canned in syrup	22	45 (1 slice)
Pistachio nuts, shelled	170	
Pizza, with cheese topping	66	268
Plaice, steamed or grilled	26	104
fried	66	264
Plums, raw	11	40 (3 medium)
stewed without sugar	6	25
canned in syrup	22	88

	cals. per 25 g/ 1 oz, 2.5 ml/ 1 fl oz	cals. per 100 g/4 oz or as stated
Rum (standard pub measure)		75
Saccharin	0	
Salad cream, regular	124	
low-calorie	50	
Salami	128	512
boiled	88	
Salmon, fresh, steamed or grilled	46	185
canned	39	115 (75 g/3 oz)
smoked	35	140
Salt	0	
Sardines, fresh, grilled	45	180
canned in oil	83	250 (75 g/3 oz)
canned in tomato sauce	56	225
Sausage		
grilled beef	78	310 (2 large)
grilled pork	93	385 (2 large)
roll	140	280 (1 medium)
Scallops, steamed	30	120
Scones	90	180 (1)
Shepherd's pie		256 (apx.)
Shortbread (per biscuit)		70 (apx.)
Skate, steamed or grilled	28	112

Olives	24	
stuffed	13	
Olive oil	265	
Omelette (2 eggs, cooked in 12 g/½ oz butter)		290
Onions		
raw or boiled	5	
raw spring	10	
cocktail, pickled	2	
fried	100	
soup	6	60 (300 ml/½ pint)
Oranges		40 (1 medium-sized)
juice, unsweetened	12	60 (150 ml/¼ pint)
squash, undiluted	40	
sparkling orange drink	12	120 (300 ml/½ pint)
Oxtail soup	13	130 (300 ml/½ pint)
Pancakes (made from 75 ml/3 fl oz batter)		180
Parsley	5	
Parsnips, boiled	15	60
Passion fruit, weighed with shell	13	102 (pulp and seeds only)
Pastry, flaky	167	
short	157	
Peaches, fresh	10	40 (1 medium)
stewed without sugar	8	32
canned in syrup	25	100

Pork		
roast leg	90	360
roast loin, lean only	81	325
chop, grilled		510
pie	105	
Potatoes		
crisps	160	
chips	70	205 (from 1 large potato)
boiled	22	90 (2 medium)
roast	35	140 (2 medium)
baked in jacket		95 (1 large)
salad (with dressing)	28	112
Prawns, shelled	30	
Prunes, dried	35	
stewed	19	75
canned in syrup	34	136
Radishes	5	
Raisins	70	
Raspberries, raw and stewed without sugar	7	30
canned in syrup	22	88
Ravioli, canned in tomato sauce	32	128
Rhubarb, stewed without sugar	1	4
canned in syrup	22	88
Rice		
plain boiled	35	
pudding	42	168

Sole, steamed or grilled	24	100
Soups		
thin, packet, depending on type		65-100 (300 ml/½ pint)
thin, canned, depending on type		70-130 (300 ml/½ pint)
thick, packet, depending on type		90-200 (300 ml/½ pint)
thick (creamed), depending on type		140-230 (300 ml/½ pint)
Southern Comfort	84	
Spaghetti, raw	102	
boiled	29	115
Spinach, boiled	7	30
Strawberries, fresh	7	30
canned in syrup	22	88
ice cream	49	98 (50 g/2 oz)
Stuffings, packet (dried)		
parsley and thyme	100	
sage and onion	96	
Suet	260	
Sugar (all types)	110	25 (1 teaspoon)
Sultanas	70	
Swedes, boiled	5	20
Sweetcorn, boiled		
on the cob		70 (1 medium)
kernels, boiled	25	
canned	28	
Syrup, golden	84	50 (1 tablespoon)
sponge pudding	94	376

	cals. per 25 g/ 1 oz, 2.5 ml/ 1 fl oz	cals. per 100 g/4 oz or as stated
Tabasco sauce		1 (¼ teaspoon)
Tangerines	10	20 (1 medium)
Tomatoes, raw or grilled	5	10 (1)
juice		25 (150 ml/¼ pint)
purée	4	
canned	9	36
soup, cream canned		160-200 (depending on type)
ketchup	30	20 (1 tablespoon)
Tongue, ox	88	335
Tonic water		50 (225-ml/8½-oz bottle)
Trifle		90 (apx.)
Trout, steamed or baked	35	140
Tuna fish, steamed	40	160
canned	72	220 (75-g/3-oz can)
Turkey, roast	56	225
Turnip, boiled	5	20
Veal		
cutlet, fried with egg and breadcrumbs	61	245
fillet, roast	66	265

	cals. per 25 g/ 1 oz, 2.5 ml/ 1 fl oz	cals. per 100 g/4 oz or as stated
Vegetables		
mixed (frozen)	16	74
soup (canned)		80-150 (300 ml/½ pint)
Vermouth, dry		110 per small glass
sweet		180 per small glass
Vinegar		1 (1 tablespoon)
cider		2 (1 tablespoon)
wine		3 (1 tablespoon)
Vodka (standard pub measure)		65
Walnuts, shelled	155	
pickled	21	
Water chestnuts	22	
Watercress	4	
Watermelon		41 (1-cm/½-inch slice)
Wheatgerm	110	
Whisky (standard pub measure)		60
Whitebait, fried	152	304 (average helping)
Whiting, steamed	26	104
White sauce	41	

	cals. per 25 g/ 1 oz, 2.5 ml/ 1 fl oz	cals. per 100 g/4 oz or as stated
Wine		
Champagne	21	105 (per glass)
dry red wine	20	95-100 (per glass)
dry white wine	18	90 (per glass)
port	44	130 (per small glass)
sherry, dry	33	100 (per small glass)
sherry, sweet	38	110 (per small glass)
sweet white wine	25	125
Worcestershire sauce		12 (1 tablespoon)
Yoghurt		
fruit	25	125 (150 ml/5 fl oz)
plain	15	75 (150 ml/5 fl oz)
Yorkshire pudding	63	252

Also by Cas Clarke

Grub on a Grant

cheap and foolproof recipes for all student appetites

Cas Clarke's bestseller contains nearly 200 tried and tested recipes, none of which will break the bank and all of which are easy to prepare and cook. From quick snacks to full-blown dinner-party dishes, the book covers such situations as:

- cooking for one
- cooking with friends
- classic student dishes
- 'seduction suppers'
- dinner parties
- the vegetarian student
- the slimming student
- what-to-eat-when-finances-are-low

What the press said:

'. . . a useful little book for an absolute beginner. My children simply loved her Varsity Pie.'

Prue Leith, *The Guardian*

'. . . written by a student who experienced the problems of cooking for herself for the first time while at university; she reckons her recipes are foolproof, and so they are.'

Daily Telegraph

'. . . a variety of cheap, imaginative recipes – the book is a must.'

The Epicurean, *Sheffield City Press*

'. . . full of extremely practical and sensible advice and some hilarious cartoons, giving an exciting repertoire of meals whatever the culinary abilities.'

Jill Probert, *Liverpool Daily Post*

'. . . dishes up oodles of good sense for those who know less about cooking than they do about Old Norse, nuclear physics or even knitting . . . amusingly illustrated . . . spans the huge expanse between beans on toast and three-course dinner parties . . . assumes no prior knowledge of cooking at all.'

Caroline Thomas, *Coventry Evening Telegraph*